TICKS
A Lay Guide to a Human Hazard

THE AUTHORS

George Hendry (PhD, DSc) is a biochemist, an ecologist and a university senior lecturer and author of over 100 original research papers. He also wrote the best-selling book *Midges in Scotland* on another of Scotland's little charmers. The sight of his four-year-old daughter coming in from the garden with fourteen ticks spurred him to link up with...

Darrel Ho-Yen (BMSc (Hons), MB, ChB, FRCPath, MD), Head of Microbiology, Raigmore Hospital NHS Trust, Director of the Scottish Toxoplasma Reference Laboratory and honorary clinical senior lecturer at Aberdeen University. He is the author of over 75 original research papers and several books. The Department at Raigmore Hospital is responsible for investigating Lyme disease in the Highlands and Islands of Scotland, an area covering 15% of the UK land mass and holding many of its ticks.

GEORGE HENDRY AND DARREL HO-YEN

Ticks

A LAY GUIDE TO A HUMAN HAZARD

First published in 1998 by Mercat Press
James Thin, 53 South Bridge, Edinburgh EH1 1YS

© George Hendry and Darrel Ho-Yen 1998

ISBN: 1873644 809

Printed and bound in Great Britain by
Athenæum Press Ltd., Gateshead, Tyne & Wear

CONTENTS

> **How to remove a tick:** 🕷
> p. 74

ILLUSTRATIONS and FIGURES

ACKNOWLEDGEMENTS

The authors wish to acknowledge the help of Dr Paul Hillyard, (Natural History Museum, London), Professor Pat Nuttall and Dot Carey (Institute of Virology and Environmental Microbiology, Oxford), Dr Gerhard Soja (Forschungszentrum Seibersdorf, Austria), Kristine MacKenzie and Chris MacKenzie (respectively Ross-shire crofter and keeper), Edmund O'Brien and Mervin Roberts (Selectmen of Old Lyme Connecticut), Dr Jim Douglas (Fort William), Alan McGinley, Kim Cahill and Debbie Gilham (Raigmore Hospital NHS Trust), the British Ecological Society and the forbearance of Tom Johnstone of Mercat Press. *Agus sine airson a'ceartach, foighidinn's gaol!*

PREAMBLE

There is a widely held expectation today that countryside holidays should be carefree, safe and healthy. The reality, however, is that, throughout rural Britain, ticks are present in significant numbers and they carry diseases. One of these, Lyme disease, has attracted publicity in Britain, in western Europe and north America in recent years. The result of this publicity is that for some people an innocent day out in the country can be marred by considerable apprehension on finding a tick quietly feeding away on the skin. For other visitors to the countryside, the feeding tick may be unexpected and unseen but if it continues to be unheeded it may well increase the risk of infection.

In this book we aim to provide authoritative, plain-language, practical information on ticks and tick-borne diseases and how to avoid them. The book is written not just for the hill walker, climber, shooter, fisher, farmer, crofter or forester but for all who seek no more than a healthy and rewarding day out in the countryside.

1
TICKS AND DISEASE—
AN INTRODUCTION
🕷

Ticks—the Background

- Ticks carry diseases afflicting livestock, wildlife and humans.
- Lyme disease is a major tick-borne disease of humans.
- Lyme disease is present in Britain, in north and central Europe and north America.
- In Britain, the micro-organism causing Lyme disease is carried by our most common tick—the sheep tick.
- The sheep tick, despite its name, feeds on deer, cattle, sheep and many smaller mammals in forests, woodland, damp pastures and moorland.

Ticks carry diseases, and one disease has made headline news in western Europe and north America in recent years—Lyme disease. But the story of tick-borne diseases is much, much older, and in most parts of the world Lyme disease is unknown. Instead in most regions ticks are known as blood-sucking parasites that carry a wide range of diseases—diseases that afflict Man, his livestock and wildlife. Globally, ticks rank as one of the most important biological limits to Man's economic activities.

Ticks and disease—a global perspective

Tick-borne diseases have been recognized for centuries and have brought untold misery and economic disaster to many parts of the world. In Britain, Scottish farmers have long suffered the devastations of louping-ill. Two hundred years ago, the Ettrick shepherd James Hogg knew this as thwarter-ill, trembling-ill or louping evil. Once thought of as a tick-borne disease peculiar to the damp pastures of Scotland it is now known from the hill country of England, Wales and from various parts of coastal Europe. Apart from destroying flocks, it afflicts humans, particularly farmers, shepherds, vets and abattoir workers.

And long before louping-ill, a disease known today as haemorrhagic fever had been recorded in Tadzhikistan from the twelfth century. In 1944 this tick-borne virus spread rapidly westwards into war-torn Ukraine, probably on the backs of hares. Characterized by fever and bleeding, the disease has now been recorded in Africa, Pakistan and more recently in southern Europe.

For all his might in war, Man's capacity for belligerency has literally been brought to a halt by ticks. In the 1970s, during the civil war in Zimbabwe, missions had to be aborted following severe outbreaks of Mediterranean spotted fever. Today this tick-borne disease is endemic to southern Europe, much of Africa and India. War also saw the spread of a tick-borne disease into southern Europe in 1940. Known at the time as Balkan gripe, and today as Q-fever, it is an occupational hazard to sheep farmers, sheep shearers and meat handlers, leading to fever, pneumonia and hepatitis if untreated. Today, it is present throughout much of Europe.

Another import is African swine fever. It was first recorded in Kenya, where farmers faced a catastrophic wipe-out of pigs before the first World War. This tick-borne virus has since spread to Spain, Portugal, France and Belgium. In Italy 100,000 pigs died or had to be slaughtered in 1967. In Malta the disease was only eradicated after the entire pig population had been destroyed.

In eastern and central Europe tick-borne encephalitis has been commonly reported in recent decades. First recognized in Russia in the 1930s, this tick-transmitted viral disease has spread westwards into central Europe and eastwards into Asia, probably with the movement of livestock. In recent years the Austrian health

authorities have been sufficiently concerned to undertake a programme of mass vaccination of children and adults.

One of the most important livestock diseases in Africa is
heartwater, which got its nineteenth-century name from the accumulation of fluid round the heart. This tick-borne disease,
characterized by fever, twitching, a high-stepping gait and convulsion, is today controlled largely by vaccination of herds. A
tick-borne disease widespread in Europe is redwater fever where
the blood of affected cattle becomes thin and watery. Transmitted by our all-too-common sheep tick, it is of considerable
economic significance—livestock losses in Ireland alone were
running at £9 million annually in the 1980s.

Wherever large herds are maintained ticks become a problem. American ranchers in the cowboy era of the mid-nineteenth
century witnessed another tick-borne disease, Texas cattle fever,
destroying up to 90% of their cattle in susceptible herds. The
ranchers themselves, and their families, were afflicted by Colorado tick fever and Rocky Mountain fever. An outbreak of the
latter in Montana in 1899, with severe illness and death among
both white settlers and native Americans, was pinned down to a
tick carried on dogs. Today, this notifiable disease is widespread
in north America, particularly in the east and, if untreated, can
be fatal. It has proved a particular hazard among children playing
in woodlands. It was the discovery in the early years of the
twentieth century that ticks were responsible for transmitting
Rocky Mountain fever, Texas cattle fever and Colorado tick fever that led to the establishment of the Rocky Mountain
Laboratories of the US Public Health Service as a centre for
tick-borne disease research. This was the research centre which
was to play a key part in the discovery of the microbe involved in
Lyme disease eighty years later.

The story of tick-borne diseases is a worldwide one of misery
and economic devastation to many millions. For most western
Europeans, however, the story would have remained a tale of

misfortune for farmers, a disease of foreign countries—that is until the advent of Lyme disease.

Lyme disease...100 years in the making

Two hours out from New York, east on Interstate 95, cross the Connecticut River, take the next exit and drive into another age. This is the world of New England classical timber and brick houses, of sailing ships and sea captains. Here the American Impressionists of the early years of the century would meet to paint, and their inspiration still lives. This is the small town of Old Lyme.

Today, as well as painters, the community attracts weekend home-owners and visitors from New York, bird watchers and duck hunters. Five minutes from the town centre visitors congregate at night to watch beavers building dams. Muskrats, coyotes and white-tailed deer are only minutes away. While the human environment is under the guardianship of the Lyme Historic Society, the Old Lyme Conservation Trust cares for the surrounding water meadows, marshes, beaches and woodlands. A New England idyll.

The idyll was shattered in November 1975. In the previous three summers, a dozen children from the small communities of 5,000 souls around Lyme had been diagnosed as having juvenile rheumatoid arthritis. Two concerned mothers, Polly Murray and Judith Mensch, could not accept the diagnosis of arthritis in child after child, up and down their roads. They went to the state health authority. Within days of their visit, new reports of arthritis were noted among other children, and several adults, in the three neighbouring townships of Lyme, Old Lyme and East Haddam. Alerted by these reports, the health authorities at nearby Yale University School of Medicine, led by Dr Allen Steere, tracked down 39 children, the youngest aged 2 years, and a dozen adults, who had recently suffered several painful bouts of

4

swelling in the knee and other joints. The attacks often persisted for only a week or two but recurred at intervals over the following months or years. Several of the attacks of arthritis had begun in the summer of 1972. The affected children were largely from the 5 to 14 year age group, with rather more boys than girls.

The symptoms, however, did not quite fit the classic description of juvenile rheumatoid arthritis. An odd coincidence also emerged. Many patients recalled that the arthritis was preceded by a large red mark or swelling on their skin which expanded in size over subsequent days. Physicians, parents and children alike put this down to an insect bite. The next clue came from maps drawn up showing the location of the houses lived in by the affected children and adults. Most houses were close to heavily wooded areas, abounding in white-tailed deer, and located on just four country roads and not in town or village centres. One in every 10 children from this rural backwater had the illness. The children attended two schools, one in Old Lyme, the other 12 miles away in East Haddam. No common exposure such as an immunization programme, a swimming pool or a particular food could be traced. More puzzlingly, perhaps, the onset of the illness occurred in different years in the same families, usually starting in the summer or early autumn.

Because some forms of arthritis are known to occur after infections, rubella and parvovirus especially, most of the patients were tested for a battery of viruses and bacteria. None showed any common pattern of infection. The possibility of a mosquito-borne virus was checked. All tests were negative. By the end of the intensive study of the original 51 patients, the summer of 1976 brought forward 38 new patients. With a total of 89 cases, the authorities needed to give it a name—and so Lyme disease was born.

Going back to the possibility of an insect bite, with a characteristic large and expanding red mark, the clinicians recalled similar reports of such marks in the European medical literature, from Sweden, France and Germany, dating way back at least as far as 1913. This red mark had been named *Erythema chronicum migrans* (ECM), medical Latin for a short-lived expanding or migrating red mark or ring. Some of these European reports linked ECM to the bite of the sheep tick, a creature not found in Connecticut. Nevertheless, the Yale rheumatologists collected 62 populations of ticks from the local community but they too were negative in the tests. By the early 1980s whatever was causing ECM in Europe and Lyme disease in Connecticut remained elusive.

The key to the mystery lay hidden in a paper on ECM written in 1923 by a Jewish-Viennese dermatologist Benjamin Lipschutz. Following the best traditions of informed hunches, Dr Lipschutz had written 'perhaps we are dealing with a skin infection caused through the bite of a tick. Therefore, attention should be directed towards microscopic and bacteriologic investigation of the intestinal tract and of the salivary gland of the tick'. Unfortunately, no-one followed up his suggestion and Lipschutz himself died, prematurely, eight years later. Had the link between ECM and ticks been established firmly, the children of Old Lyme and East Haddam could have been given antibiotic treatment, without ever going on to develop arthritis.

With hindsight, what became known as Lyme disease in the USA in the late 1970s has been there in the European medical records for the best part of a century. A characteristic skin lesion, which we know today from Lyme disease patients, was described as early as 1883 in a 36-year-old man. He had had the lesion for 16 years—pushing the disease back to 1867. The mark on the skin superficially resembled syphilis—itself a serious concern in the pre-antibiotic age. By 1910, 134 patients in Austria had been described with what we know today as Lyme disease. But, apart from the odd report from recent European immigrants, it was unknown in the United States.

During the 1920s Swedish, French, German and Austrian physicians began to link ECM with other features of Lyme disease and—an important point—some patients recalled an earlier incident of being bitten by a tick. But still no progress had been made on the cause—was it a virus, bacterium or toxic material carried by ticks? By the late 1940s several hundred cases of what was to be eventually called Lyme disease had been described in western Europe, firmly linking ECM with a wide range of muscular and neurological disorders—sometimes persisting only for several weeks or months. Then, after months or years of recovery some patients relapsed, often with rheumatic disease, forms of meningitis or heart disease. On questioning, many patients could recall an earlier tick bite. By the early 1960s, German and Czech physicians, now with several hundred cases to work from, showed that the incidence of ECM-related disorders overlapped with the geographical distribution of the sheep tick.

While the Europeans were linking ECM with ticks, four thousand miles away in the summer of 1969, a young physician was bitten by a tick while hunting grouse in Wisconsin. Within days he became the first diagnosed case of ECM in north America; by good fortune he was treated by a colleague familiar with ECM in Europe. Meanwhile, back in Old Lyme, Polly Murray had begun to notice an increase in unexplained diseases among her neighbourhood children. A case of ECM was reported from north California, then in 1975 a cluster of three, then four more cases appeared in south-east Connecticut. Further up the coast the good townsfolk of Old Lyme were, unknowingly, about to make their name known world-wide.

Six years on and the story now moves offshore. Opposite Old Lyme lies Long Island. Here, in the summer of 1981, the Swiss-American Willi Burgdorfer was down on his knees hunting for ticks involved in a different tick-borne disease—a spotted fever. He was unsuccessful. However, a colleague gave him some deer ticks from Shelter Island, 18 miles due south of Old Lyme and by then an established area of Lyme disease. Two ticks out of 44 showed poorly-stained clumps of irregularly coiled bacteria known as spirochetes. With help from the Rocky Mountain Laboratories, a long-established research centre for tick diseases, the spirochetes were successfully cultured. Blood samples from Shelter Island residents showed that some carried antibodies to this spirochete. And by extraordinary coincidence, similar, if not identical, spirochetes had been found by Dr Burgdorfer three years earlier in western Switzerland, a hot-spot for ECM. Like all true-life breakthroughs other laboratories were close behind. Within 12 months of Willi Burgdorfer's discovery, the spirochete was found in ECM patients in Germany and then in samples of European sheep ticks.

The spirochete was named *Borrelia burgdorferi* in honour of Willi Burgdorfer and proved to be closely related to a number of other borrelias all of which are carried by ticks, the majority causing a group of diseases called relapsing fevers.

The final piece of the puzzle was to find the source of the spirochete. Ticks live on blood and most probably acquired the spirochete when feeding on an animal host. The question was, which animal? Within three years, the spirochete had been found in field mice in Europe, the white-footed mouse in Connecticut and subsequently in deer and many other wild and domesticated animals on both sides of the Atlantic. The pieces of the puzzle were all there: the spirochete microbe, the mammalian host as the source or reservoir, the tick as the transmitter and finally Lyme disease itself.

Lyme disease today

In all probability, Lyme disease has been present in Europe for centuries, largely unrecognized. Why it appears to have spread so rapidly in New England is less certain; how much is a real geographical spread of the disease and how much is due to increased public awareness is not known. Western Europe and north America have seen a considerable expansion in rural recreation in recent years—camping, rambling, hill-walking, game hunting and fishing, with many more people exposed to ticks than just farming and forestry workers. Changes in land-use with return of pasture to woodland, particularly in New England, have brought deer and deer ticks closer to human habitation. In parts of western Europe the deer population has increased greatly in recent decades. A spread of the spirochete itself is a real possibility, certainly within the United States and probably in parts of western Europe. Transmission of the spirochete from Europe to north America and beyond in recent decades could have occurred, though so far there is no direct evidence to support this—indeed, the north American spirochete shows distinct differences from its European counterpart, both in molecular make-up and in the form of the disease it causes in humans.

Wherever the spirochete came from, by 1988 Lyme disease had become the most common animal-borne infection of humans in the United States with some 16,000 new cases reported in 1996 alone, up from 12,000 cases the year before. In just 10 years it had been recorded in 47 states. Several thousand cases are now being reported each summer throughout northern, western and central Europe, with smaller numbers from southern Europe, China, Japan and Australia. By 1990, surveys of infected ticks showed that the spirochete was widespread. Today it is known to be present in every European country.

Lyme disease in Britain

In Britain, a survey conducted by the Institute of Virology at Oxford found that one-third of ticks collected from 230 sites in rural Britain proved positive in a test for the spirochete causing Lyme disease. The survey is incomplete and, indeed, has a bias towards Scotland and certain forested areas of England. The laboratory test used to detect the DNA of the spirochete may also have overstated the incidence of the spirochete. The important point, however, is that these results and those from other surveys indicate that Lyme disease is probably widespread in Britain and, from the experience in other countries, it is here to stay.

Many species of wild animals appear to support spirochete-infested ticks in Britain. In a survey of red and roe deer from 27 sites in Scotland, Wales and England, the spirochete was found in at least one tick from every site. Not surprisingly, people working in deer territory are at risk of acquiring the spirochete following a tick bite. A 1990 survey of field staff from the Red Deer Commission, Forestry Commission and the then Nature Conservancy Council showed that 25% of workers had antibodies to the spirochete. A review of Scottish Natural Heritage field workers found that 26% of those working on the west coast island of Rum, with its large red deer population, carried antibodies to the spirochete, double that of their colleagues working in the east. In England, 20% of forest workers in Thetford and 29% of New Forest Rangers gave positive reactions in tests. While there may be some problems with false positives in these tests, they do confirm that Lyme disease can be an occupational hazard. And not just an occupational hazard—in the same New Forest of southern England, one in ten inhabitants in a localized survey carry antibodies to the spirochete, against one in 50 in a control group of city-dwellers. But city-dwellers are also at risk—screening of urban park workers in Richmond and Bushey Parks in London, each with a large deer population, showed that 16 out of 44 workers had high spirochete antibody levels. Today, tick-borne diseases in Britain no longer consist only of curiously named diseases like the louping-ill of the northern hills; the spirochetes causing Lyme disease are widespread throughout the island.

Lyme disease—the American legacy

Old Lyme, Connecticut, may have given its name to a disease widespread in north America and Europe, but it has also generated research and health care in its name. In Connecticut today, the Lyme Disease Foundation and state-based drug companies distribute information leaflets warning of Lyme disease. Through radio, television and newspapers efforts are made each year to promote public awareness of ticks and of tick-borne diseases. Plain-language leaflets are available throughout the United States with advice on personal protection and on how to spot the symptoms of Lyme disease. Local physicians are well aware of the disease and, if it is detected early, can treat it effectively with antibiotics. This, then, is the legacy of Polly Murray's action, twenty years ago. We Europeans are the beneficiaries.

Tick facts

- All ticks obtain their food by sucking the blood of mammals, birds or reptiles.
- Hungry ticks search for hosts (e.g. walkers with bare arms or legs) by clinging on to the tops of grasses, bracken, shrubs and bushes.
- Ticks vary greatly in size—from smaller than a pin-head to the size of a small drawing pin and in colour from black to brown, grey or dark golden-red.
- Ticks carry a greater range of diseases than any other invertebrate pest.
- Ticks acquire and transmit disease-causing microrganisms during feeding.
- People most at risk from tick-borne diseases include farmers, dairymen, crofters, shepherds and sheep shearers, stalkers, gamekeepers, livestock transporters, abattoir workers, foresters, fencing contractors, country-side rangers, naturalists and ecologists.
- Recreations at risk include countryside walking, hill walking, angling, shooting, bird watching, camping and caravanning.
- In Britain, ticks bite humans from spring to autumn; left undisturbed ticks feed for several days.
- When not feeding, ticks shelter in vegetation where they may survive for a year or more without food.

What are ticks?

Ticks are related to spiders, scorpions, mites and harvestmen (daddy-long-legs). Unlike insects, adult ticks have eight legs, do not fly and lack antennae. All ticks, without exception, are blood-sucking parasites giving nothing beneficial back to their hosts. And very successful parasites they are too.

Ticks have been known to Man from earliest records. Over 2,000 years ago Aristotle catalogued the sheep tick as a 'disgusting parasitic animal'. And the sheep tick, from archaeological evidence, seems to have been an early immigrant to Iceland along with the first European settlers. While the Saxons seem to have had only one (polite) word for ticks, *ticca*, the Scottish Gaels evolved many more—*gartan, mial-caorach, sar, sealan, seileann, uamhag*, reflecting perhaps their greater exposure to tick-infested livestock.

Today we know that, world-wide, the number and range of diseases carried by ticks probably exceeds all other invertebrates. Ticks carry many disease-causing micro-organisms (viruses, bacteria or minute worms) picked up during feeding on one host and subsequently transmitted during feeding to a second host. Once the microbe enters the host's blood stream, other ticks feeding on the same host may themselves become infected. In this way, in many tick-borne diseases, the host, usually a mammal or bird, becomes the reservoir of infection while the tick acts as the transmitter of the disease. In other cases the micro-organism may pass from one generation of ticks to another through its fertilized eggs, the tick serving both as the reservoir and transmitter. In the case of Lyme disease, the most important reservoirs are believed to be small mammals, on which ticks feed early in their life. In Britain, mice, voles, squirrels, hedgehogs and birds serve to support the young ticks and carry the disease-causing micro-organism thereafter. Reservoirs for nymphs and adult ticks include sheep, cattle, horses, deer, cats, dogs, foxes and, at least in southern Britain, pheasants. The important point is that it is the tick which transmits the disease from host to host.

Ticks evolved alongside land animals about 400 million years ago and today infest almost all mammals, birds, reptiles and amphibians. Ticks found on the fossilized remains of a woolly rhino, that lived two million years ago, are indistinguishable from tick species present today. Ticks certainly infested the dinosaurs until those reptiles became extinct 70 million years ago. By then some ticks had adapted to furry mammals by evolving spurs at the top of their legs, the better to grip hairy bodies. Today about 850 species of tick so far have been described world-wide. They fall into two major groups, hard ticks and soft ticks. Some 22 species have been recorded in Britain (see the *Appendix*) with 12 in Scotland. However, what Scotland lacks in variety, it makes up for in numbers—where one species, the sheep tick (*Ixodes ricinus*) is abundant in the extensive tracts of damp hill pastures and moorlands.

Ticks are not, however, just a countryside hazard. The hedgehog tick (*Ixodes hexagonus*) became a pest of underground air-raid shelters in London during World War II. The passerine tick (*Ixodes frontalis*) infests many birds in city parks and gardens while the pigeon tick (*Argas reflexus*) has been long established in such places as Canterbury Cathedral. A Scots tick of pigeons, *Ixodes caledonicus*, was first discovered in the (former) coal mining and iron-foundry town of Denny, Stirlingshire. In contrast, the territory of the seabird tick (*Ixodes uriae*) extends from St Kilda to the Bass Rock, and from Shetland to the Isle of Wight. However, the species most likely to be met in rural Britain and indeed throughout western and central Europe is the sheep tick (*Ixodes ricinus*). It is also the main vector for Lyme disease in Europe. The account which follows refers largely to this species.

What does a tick look like?

To first-time observers the outstanding feature of the sheep tick is its extreme range of size (Figure 2.1). The larva, differing from the adult in having just six legs, is smaller than a pin head, more like a fleck of soot. The next stage, the nymph, is about the

Larva

Nymph

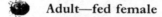 Adult—unfed male

Adult—unfed female

Adult—fed female

Figure 2.1: The approximate size of the sheep tick *Ixodes ricinus* in its different developmental stages. The nymph is the form most frequently encountered biting humans

size of a pin head and it is the nymph that is the one most frequently met with by humans. The adult female, less common on humans, is about 3 to 4 mm in diameter before feeding but in her fully engorged state she may expand to 10 mm, the size and shape of a flattened raisin (Figure 2.2).

Ticks appear to the eye to be all of one piece consisting of a flattened oval-shaped black, brown, sometimes grey-brown or dark golden-red body. When feeding, the pointed end is buried firmly into the skin of its host, the back end stuck up in the air. Closer examination with a magnifying glass will reveal its walking legs poking out at the side. If there is any doubt, the rule is that if you find a small black spot on your skin which was not there yesterday and does not readily brush off, and particularly if the skin around it is reddish, it is a tick!

Tick biting and feeding

The tick year in Britain starts in spring, with larvae, nymphs and adults emerging from their over-wintering sites deep in vegetation

15

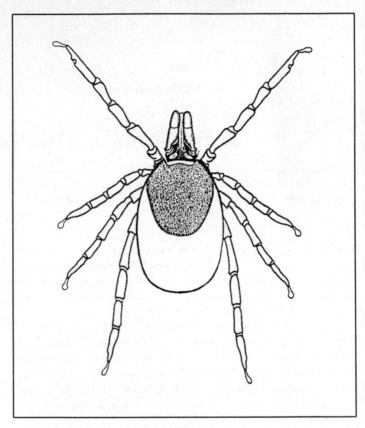

Figure 2.2: A drawing of a female adult sheep tick enlarged about 15-fold (adapted from Hillyard, 1996, Natural History Museum, London)

and crevices in the soil. They begin their journey usually in damp weather by climbing to the top of grasses, bracken, heather and small shrubs. There they adopt their host-searching or questing position. When searching for a host, the tick clings to the top of its plant, gently waving its front pair of legs. On these legs it has a remarkably sensitive set of sensors which monitor changes in temperature, humidity, odours, particularly carbon dioxide, as well as air-borne vibration. Sheep ticks lack eyes though they appear to respond to passing shadows.

Once they have detected the presence of and grabbed hold of passing animals, or human legs or clothing, they move fast. On a smooth surface they can travel six inches in ten seconds. In order to attach themselves to their hosts, ticks first use their leg spurs to grip onto hair or clothing. On humans they will seek out soft spots—behind the knee, in the groin, tummy button, armpits, crook of the arm, neck—or the comparative safety of the head. On other mammals and birds ticks tend to congregate round the head and neck in areas where the host finds it difficult to lick, scratch or peck.

Ticks talk to other ticks, using not sound but a chemical language. Pheromones—information-bearing chemicals—are used to pass on data about food gathering, assembly, mating, regulation of social organization and host finding. Much research has focused on these pheromones and their sensors because they may, one day, offer a sensitive and effective way of controlling the behaviour of ticks.

Once on board its host and a suitable site established, the tick pushes its head down, back end up at a sharp angle, and bites. The minute head comes complete with a pair of articulated sharply-toothed skin cutters. The cutters are coupled to sensors which provide information on both the force required to cut through skin and on the composition of the blood. Once the cut has been opened up the tick thrusts its barbed headpiece, or hypostome, into the wound to serve as an anchor. Within minutes the tick secretes a rubbery glue which later cements the head tightly to the skin making the tick difficult to dislodge.

Ticks feed by ripping and tearing through the skin layers into the blood vessels. They then suck up the fluids that exude from the wound using their powerful pharynx. Ticks, particularly sheep ticks, are, however, slow feeders taking several days to complete a meal. Only in the final day of feeding are large quantities of blood taken up—what has been called 'the big sip'—during which the tick, particularly the female adult, expands enormously. To enjoy an uninterrupted flow of blood the tick needs to keep the wound open and to suppress the immune response of its host. It does this by incorporating into its saliva a cocktail of potent pharmaceuticals which are pumped into the wound. It is this same saliva which can contain the infectious micro-organisms which make ticks such important transmitters of disease.

Successful feeding over several days is a hazardous time for the tick. Not least the tick has to overcome the host's natural response to a wound. The tick does this by injecting through its mouth parts some powerful drugs which prevent blood clotting and suppress constriction of the wounded blood vessels and inhibit the host's other immune defences. Anti-inflammatory chemicals in the tick saliva also attempt to reduce the host's awareness of the tick. Indeed, most humans are not aware that they are being bitten. At best a gentle tickling sensation may develop some hours after attachment. Left undisturbed, the larval and nymph stages feed for 3 to 6 days.

The adult female needs over two weeks to complete her feeding, during which she will consume up to 100 times her body-weight of blood. Either before or during feeding she will be mated, just once, by a roving male. When fully fed the tick drops off, the larvae and nymphs hide in the vegetation and moult, while the adult female seeks shelter on the soil surface to lay her eggs before finally expiring.

No blood-sucking insect can match ticks during feeding. A fully engorged female tick may have consumed 3 to 4 mls of blood over several years. Mosquitoes, clegs and midges take less than 1000th of a ml over a few weeks, at best. Ticks, in large enough numbers, can and do bleed an animal to death—heavily infected seabirds, calves and lambs particularly.

Blood letting apart, ticks can carry and transmit a wide range of viruses, bacteria, fungi, protozoa and nematodes. No insect transmits such a variety of infections. Unlike almost all bloodsucking invertebrates, ticks can store their blood meal in their intestine often for months without digesting it, making this a favourable environment for the survival of pathogenic organisms.

Sheep ticks spend the active part of their two or three years of life searching for and consuming blood meals. The newly hatched larva seeks out small mammals, typically mice, shrews and voles, but if chance presents itself the larva will certainly attack humans, particularly bare-legged walkers, bare-armed vets, farmers and shepherds. Once fed, the larva drops off into the vegetation, hides, moults and re-emerges as a nymph, this time to feed, typically, on sheep, rabbits, dogs and cats, squirrels, birds and, again if chance prevails, on humans. And once again, when replete the nymph drops off its second host and hides in the vegetation, where it moults this time into the adult sexual stage. The adult, in turn, now searches for larger animals, such as deer, sheep and cattle. Well, that is the theory. In practice, ticks at all three life stages seem to grab whatever is passing. Sheep, cattle, deer and humans certainly harbour all three forms (Figure 2.3).

Because ticks feed on a range of hosts they inevitably acquire and pass on many infectious agents to other animals. They could hardly have been better designed. Once firmly attached, ticks feed slowly, giving any micro-organisms plenty of time to migrate from the host into the tick or from the tick into host. It is no coincidence that ticks with the widest taste in hosts are usually the most important carriers of infections. Again because they are slow feeders, firmly cemented onto their hosts, ticks are readily transported with livestock. Ticks and tick-borne diseases are all too easily moved from farm to farm or region to region. Migrating birds will move ticks across continents.

Ticks at rest and reproduction

Ticks are often remarkably long-lived, unlike most insects. Some species of soft ticks feeding on seabirds are known to survive for a decade or more. The sheep tick can survive for up to four years in cold areas of the north and two or three years in warmer areas. Their biting activity occurs in two phases, spring and autumn. In Scotland, north England and Wales the nymphs and adults engage in host-seeking in April and May when the air temperatures reaches about 7°C. This may be followed by a second round of biting activity in autumn. Further south the biting season starts in March, or in colder parts of Scotland seasonal activity may be

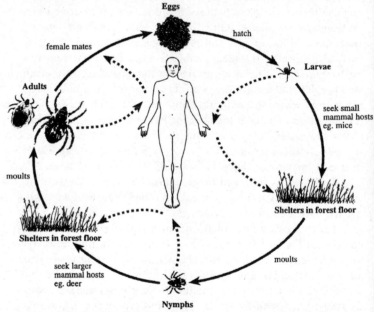

Figure 2.3 The life cycle of the sheep tick *Ixodes ricinus* from egg, to larva, to nymph and adult. The dotted lines show opportunistic feeding on a human.

delayed until June and July. Eggs are laid in mid- to late summer and may hatch within a few weeks to give rise to a second bout of biting in autumn. Or the eggs may remain as eggs throughout winter. At the end of autumn the tick larvae and nymphs shut down all activity and over-winter, the survivors resuming their quest as hungry individuals the following spring. This ability to shut down—called diapause—enables the tick to survive adverse environments and to synchronize development, feeding and reproduction with periods of maximum food availability. Come spring, warmer weather and the availability of fresh blood meals, the ticks break from diapause and go a-hunting, or questing as it is known in the trade.

Hunger drives the tick to start questing. Here the tick adopts the ambush strategy, clinging onto the tops of grasses or bracken with its back legs. Its forelegs slowly fold and unfold, gently gathering information on smells, body heat or vibration of a passing host. As the host approaches the tick claws the air more quickly. If physical contact is made, the now excited tick grasps its host firmly and scuttles up the leg or flank, through hair, fur, under clothing and within minutes begins the task of feeding. Days later when fully fed, the tick detaches from its host and returns to the vegetation to moult or lay eggs. The process of moulting in ticks is gradual and enables any micro-organisms in the tick's gut to pass from larva to nymph, nymph to adult, something which does not occur in many rapidly moulting disease-carrying insects. A tick unable to find a host after questing for hours or days will return to the moist undergrowth to regain body water. Once re-hydrated it climbs up the vegetation to its questing site—individual ticks have been recorded making this journey up to 20 times in a season. And if all else fails and there is no ready meal, the tick will batten down and fast for months, even a year.

Ticks are long-lived, particularly in cool northern areas, and frequently outlive the lambs and calves on which they feed. The

Figure 2.4: Tick-infested rough grazing in the west Highlands. Note the questing opportunities offered by tall bracken, the shade effects from nearby trees which reduce desiccation and the nearby grazed grassland supporting sheep and deer; altogether an ideal habitat for sheep ticks.

final weeks of life for the mated, fully fed, adult female tick is spent laying several thousand individually waterproofed eggs, deep in damp vegetation or in moist cracks in the soil. During egg-laying the increasingly exhausted female shrivels to half her replete body weight and then expires—a true egg-laying machine converting blood products to new progeny. No blood-sucking insect can match ticks in fecundity.

Where ticks are to be found

Although the sheep tick is well-adapted to living in Man-altered environments, it seems that the ancestral home for this species was the forest. Indeed, on the continent, our sheep tick is known as the wood tick. In deforested Britain the sheep tick is abundant in sheep and cattle pastures and especially in rough grazings in high rainfall areas of the west. It is, however, plentiful in woods and plantations throughout Britain. Moorland, hills and forests grazed by deer are often notorious for ticks. And with walkers specially in mind ticks can reach high numbers in the vegetation bordering footpaths.

Enormous numbers of ticks can be present in suitable locations. In one forest site in Austria the number of sheep tick larvae was estimated at about 200,000 per hectare, with about 90,000 nymphs and 10,000 adults. We have recorded twice this number on short stretches of vegetation flanking footpaths in Scottish hills. The major limit to tick numbers, in Britain, is drought. Most European ticks are very sensitive to water loss, particularly in periods of warm weather. The sheep tick is adapted to damp conditions and has a rather leaky outer skin or cuticle making it particularly prone to desiccation. Exposure to prolonged dry conditions forces the tick to abandon questing and to seek refuge in damp soil or vegetation. Prolonged dry periods are likely greatly to reduce the tick population. It may be fortunate that our British ticks cannot emulate camel ticks which survive for considerable periods buried in the sands of the Nile!

The sheep tick, despite its name, feeds on many kinds of wild and domestic animals, humans too when available. Humans are not, however, the main host but from a human perspective this may not always seem so. Even though sheep ticks are more likely to feed on livestock, almost any walker in the Highlands and Southern Uplands of Scotland, in Wales, north and south-west England will encounter ticks, particularly nymphs, between April and October. The incidence of sheep ticks may well be less on the cereal-growing drier east coast, but wherever cattle, sheep and deer graze, ticks will be present. Nor will humans be spared if they walk in woodland almost anywhere in the land. Ticks are a fact of country life—and not just British life. Forests and open countryside walks almost anywhere in France, Germany,

Switzerland and Austria will yield as many ticks as in Britain, if not more.

Inevitably, certain occupations are particularly at risk from tick bites, sheep shearing perhaps more than most. Sheep ticks regularly bite farmers, crofters, dairymen and shepherds. Vets, deer stalkers, game keepers, livestock transport drivers and abattoir workers are all too familiar with ticks. Even those not involved in handling animals can expect to be bitten—particularly foresters, fencing contractors, countryside rangers, roadmen, electricity and telephone linesmen, railway gangers, footpath gangs, naturalists and ecologists working in rural areas. Most of these folk are familiar with ticks and know what to do when they see an immobile black spot fastened on to their skin!

It is the unsuspecting visitors to the country who may be surprised by ticks—particularly in this age of high expectations of carefree, healthy rural holidays. The reality is that campers, caravanners, ramblers, climbers, hill walkers, bird watchers, anglers and game shooters must expect to be bitten by ticks almost anywhere in rural Britain. Their opposite numbers in Connecticut and elsewhere in north America have been well primed by health education campaigns to look for and to remove ticks promptly. This book attempts to do just that on this side of the Atlantic!

3
INFECTIONS FROM TICKS

Approach to tick infections

- Risks of infection need to be understood.
- All risks are not equal.
- All infections are not the same.
- Travel abroad involves a greater exposure to infections.
- Risks of infections may be reduced by sensible behaviour.
- Risks of infection need to be balanced against the pleasure of the activity.

After a tick bite, an individual may develop many infections. Similarly, if one buys a lottery ticket, it is possible to win several prizes. However, for the vast majority of individuals who receive a tick bite (as with most who buy a lottery ticket), the result is that there is no change in their circumstances! Whilst it is easy to understand the lottery, many find it difficult to know why all tick bites do not result in one or more infections. The explanation is in an understanding of the process of transmission of infection from ticks to humans.

Transmission of infection occurs only when several conditions have been satisfied. These mainly involve the habitat, the tick and the human being. The place where the tick bite occurs is important—the local environmental conditions may favour tick survival and some infections may thrive in certain places. The tick itself may not be infected or it may not be attached to the human host for long enough for infection to be transmitted. Lastly, some individuals are more susceptible to tick bites: perhaps because of their body odour, body heat, softness of skin, ease of attachment of tick or some other factor. Previous chapters have considered many aspects of the habitat and the tick: however,

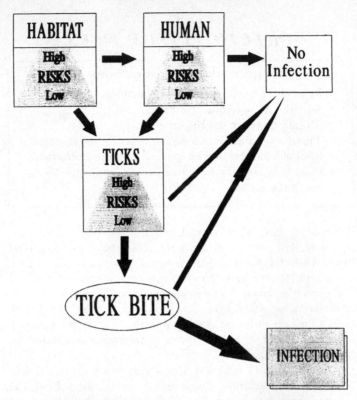

Figure 3.1. The human simply visiting the right habitat, even with the presence of ticks, will not become infected—a tick bite is necessary before there is any chance of infection. Nevertheless, many tick bites do not result in infection.

this chapter will focus on how such factors affect the development of infections.

The winning of the lottery is influenced by the odds: the more tickets one buys, the greater the chance of winning. Infections from ticks are also influenced by the odds, but for infections it is usually referred to as 'risks'. Thus for the habitat, the tick and the human, there are low and high risk factors which influence the development of any infection (Figure 3.1).

The habitat

Ticks like particular living conditions (micro-environment) and this plays an important part in determining the distribution of ticks. Humans get bitten when they invade the tick's habitat. If individuals are aware of the tick's preferred micro-environment, it is possible to avoid places with high tick populations. As ticks may have to survive for prolonged periods without a meal, it is critical that the micro-environment is not hostile to the tick. Temperatures must not be extreme and relative humidity is important. Therefore, humans may reduce the risk of tick bites by walking on tops of hills/mountains rather than at the bottom; or walking in short grass/vegetation rather than long grass/scrubland.

Geography is important. For temperate areas of the world, the longer days and raised temperatures encourage ticks to start questing for hosts. In tropical areas, where daylight and temperatures do not vary as much, the stimulus for tick activity may be the change from dry to rainy seasons. Nevertheless, it must be remembered that even during times of peak tick activity, periods of questing may have to be alternated with periods of re-hydration. Further, ticks may become dormant (diapause) if weather conditions are particularly adverse; this ability has been particularly useful in extending tick survival. It is no surprise that ticks are able to survive longer without food or water than any other group of arthropods. Throughout the world, tick populations depend on the combination of a favourable micro-environment and the presence of suitable hosts for blood meals. Avoidance of areas with this combination of factors greatly reduces the risk of developing infections.

Ticks are seasonal creatures. The risk of getting a tick bite varies with the time of year. Unfortunately, different species of ticks have different seasonal behaviour, but usually the pattern is the same for any one place. As always, local people are generally aware of the seasonal behaviour of the local ticks. With the sheep tick, there is high risk during every year: in England and Wales, spring and autumn are the two danger periods with peak tick activity; for Scotland, warmer temperatures are slightly delayed so there tends to be one period with peak tick activity in late spring-early summer. As the micro-environment is the main consideration, the seasonal peak in spring on exposed, open land may follow that on sheltered, protected land by several weeks. The converse occurs in autumn. Although general statements can be made about the seasons, it is not the time of year but the micro-environment which is important, so a warm spring may have the same characteristics as a cold summer. Within the seasonal peak of tick activity, there are also considerable variations in the peaks of the different stages of ticks (larvae, nymphs, adults). Thus, for each place there is a spectrum of increasing risk of tick bites over several months. In Canada, there is the winter tick (*Dermacentor albipictus*) whose peak activity is from November to April. If someone wants to wander into the tick's habitat at times of peak activity, it is wise to take appropriate precautions to reduce tick bites. In several countries, especially the United States and Canada, governments have taken preventative measures to reduce tick populations (Chapter 6). Walkers in these areas can be reassured that the risks of infection are significantly reduced as a result of these measures.

The tick

Large tick populations in a given place increase the risk of tick bites and the possibility of infection. It can be difficult to estimate the size of the tick population and this is dependent on the season (Chapter 2). Nevertheless, it can be useful to have some understanding of the relative numbers. In one study there were some 400,000 ticks per hectare with a distribution of 70 larvae: 20 nymphs: 1 adult. Fortunately, about 90% of those ticks were not actively questing for hosts. The adult tick population is obviously influenced by the micro-environment, but perhaps the most important factor is the size of the small mammal population which supports the nymphal ticks and allows development into adults. It is also the nymphs that may be undetected on the human because of their small size, and so they are more likely to transmit infection.

The tick population is reduced by many natural predators. In Africa and the Caribbean, 'tick birds' walk along the backs of large cattle eating any obvious ticks. Chickens are able to remove ticks from cattle as well as from the undergrowth; one study showed that each chicken was able to consume 80 ticks per hour. Apart from birds, ants and beetles can consume significant numbers of ticks. Tick numbers may also be reduced if they themselves become parasitized, such as when the chalcid wasp lays its eggs in an engorged tick which subsequently dies as the wasp larvae develop. Thus, areas rich in tick predators are likely to have lower risks of tick bites. These areas tend to be those supporting a rich wild-life (some moorlands and forests) in contrast to heavily managed arable land.

Whereas most tick species feed only on specific hosts, ticks that can transmit infections to humans are able to feed on several hosts. Nevertheless the human is not usually the main or preferred host, but rather a convenient, opportunistic blood meal. Simply, the human is in the wrong place at the wrong time. Once bitten, the time a tick spends on the host will vary: many feed within 2-3 days, but others may take much longer. Humans may make use of this delay in feeding: if ticks are removed within 12 hours of becoming attached, infection is avoided. Even if tick removal is delayed to 48 hours, infection may not occur.

The important lesson is to inspect the body after a venture within tick territory.

As a relatively small number of ticks are infected and there may not be many opportunities for new ticks to become infected, it is somewhat surprising that infections are propagated and do not die out. A part of the answer is that many infections invade the ovaries of ticks and so can infect thousands of eggs, each of which on hatching may subsequently pass on the infection. This method of infecting the ovaries is believed to be important in the transmission of infection, especially with infections such as babesiosis. Fortunately, infection of the ovaries is erratic or there would be even more infected ticks. The relative importance of a tick biting an infected host and subsequently transmitting the infection to another host is unknown.

Another method of maintaining infected ticks in a given place is when the infectious organism invades the salivary glands of an immature tick. The result is that subsequent stages of the tick, such as the nymph, can be infectious and transmit disease. If the infection had not established itself in the salivary glands, subsequent stages of the tick might not have been infectious. Thus, infection of the ovaries and salivary glands allows the infectious agent to be maintained in a particular area for several generations of ticks which may span many years. It is thus possible for local people to be aware that certain areas of the countryside are infected by a particular micro-organism. Fortunately, only a small number of humans will become infected compared to other animals—those humans who have wandered into tick territory without taking appropriate precautions against becoming infected.

The human

If humans avoid the habitat of ticks, they will not get bitten by a tick, and there will be no risk of infection (Figure 3.1). If they do go to places with a tick population, tick bites can be avoided by simple measures such as total coverage of the body, which is very effective if somewhat uncomfortable. Inevitably, there are compromises for comfort so only the lower body is usually covered, or repellents (Chapter 6) are rubbed on the legs to discourage tick bites.

For ticks to be successful in obtaining blood meals, they have to overcome the human's body defences against bleeding and the presence of foreign material. After an injury, blood vessels contract and the blood clots around the injury to prevent further bleeding. To overcome this defence mechanism, ticks release from their salivary glands several substances which dilate blood vessels and increase blood flow (prostaglandins). Also, the tick injects into the bite substances that stop blood clotting (anticoagulants). Thus, the tick is adept at overcoming human body defences which prevent bleeding.

The human's natural protection against foreign organisms (immune system) is more difficult to by-pass. The tick is most successful with hosts with whom it has associated for hundreds of years. Simply, with time the tick has been able to find ways of by-passing the host's immune system. Thus, some animals can have numerous tick bites without developing immune reactions, for example white-footed mice with the tick *I. dammini*, whereas *I. dammini* can produce a severe immune reaction in meadow voles.

The immune reactions of hosts, including humans, are complex. Two components of the immune system have to be considered: non-specific (which respond to any foreign material entering the body) and specific (directed against individual foreign material). With a first exposure to foreign material (for example, saliva from ticks), there are mainly immediate non-specific responses. Initially, there is a non-specific immune response with inflammation (redness, itchiness and swelling of the skin) which interferes with tick feeding. These immediate non-specific responses depend on several blood cells but can also be reduced by drugs, such as anti-histamines. Over the next 2–3 weeks the human body starts to develop several specific protective proteins (antibodies) against the tick saliva. Subsequently, these individuals are regarded as immune and after a second tick bite will produce immediate interaction between these antibodies and tick saliva. There is a specific response with the area of the tick bite becoming filled with watery fluid instead of red blood cells. The result is that the tick's red blood cell meal is dramatically reduced. Further, this inadequate meal can result in direct damage to the tick and prevent its subsequent development. These mechanisms are useful for humans who have repeated tick bites, whereas humans who rarely have tick bites will not have a vigorous immune reaction and so be at higher risks of infection. Ticks that remain attached to an immune individual feed slowly or not at all and may die as they are unable to feed. In addition, the itchiness of the site and prolonged attachment predispose to the tick being removed by the host's scratching. However, some young deer may have so much blood removed by tick bites that the deer dies without mounting an immune response because the tick–deer relationship is long-standing.

The position of the tick and the human is quite different as humans are usually accidental hosts for the tick. Yet it is still noticeable that humans who have frequent contact with ticks often do not have evidence of many tick-borne infections. A likely explanation is that these humans have developed immune reactions to a tick attachment which interfere with feeding. Several substances may initiate the immune reaction to ticks, for example the cement with which the tick attaches to the host or saliva from the tick. Similarly, in animals that are not frequent hosts for ticks, it requires repeated tick bites before the animal has circulating antibodies which are able to act immediately and reduce tick attachment, feeding and the blood meal. The time of attachment and length of feeding can therefore be influenced by the human's immune system.

Individuals who have developed immunity to tick saliva may be in the best position as their immune system may interfere with tick attachment and feeding and so prevent the tick passing any infections to these individuals. Those persons who have had a particular infection before may only be immune to developing that same infection again, but be susceptible to tick bites and the development of other infections. As in Figure 3.1, infections can only result in a susceptible human who is in a place with ticks and who gets bitten by an infected tick. In addition, the tick must be attached long enough to transmit infection and the human's immune system must have failed to prevent the infection from being established.

Infections

It is easy to understand that if one does not get a tick bite, or if the tick is not infected, there will be no infection (Figure 3.1). However, it can be more difficult to understand that an infected tick bite may not result in infection. The problem is in understanding the term 'infectious dose'. Simply, this means that unless there are sufficient infectious organisms transmitted in the tick bite, no infection will result. Small numbers of infectious organisms can be easily destroyed by the human immune system, whereas large numbers are too much for the immune system of susceptible individuals.

Infections transmitted by ticks can be classified into three groups, mainly dependent on size: viruses, bacteria and larger organisms. Viruses are very small organisms which are not visible to the human eye without a very powerful microscope; viruses also require to invade living cells before they can multiply. Bacteria are much bigger and do not need living cells to multiply. Larger organisms vary tremendously in their size and complexity and are, essentially, all of the other infectious organisms apart from viruses and bacteria. In this book, tick infections will be considered in these three groups. However, it should be remembered that the requirements of viruses, bacteria and larger organisms for survival vary enormously. The presence of particularly favourable growing conditions in the tick will allow perpetuation of certain infections.

Humans can be preoccupied with whether or not they develop a particular infection (e.g. Lyme disease, louping ill). However, the development of any infection is a result of a complex process in which very many factors interact. The individual should recognise that many criteria must be fulfilled before one gets infected. The process may be interrupted at several points and therefore one should not worry disproportionately. To return to our lottery analogy, when one buys a lottery ticket it is premature to worry about how one may spend a jackpot of millions of pounds. It is best to worry when you see your winning numbers. Then, if you feel that you might not cope with having millions of pounds, you simply do not claim your prize. One objective of this book is to provide the information so that one knows when one should be worried, and what options are available at each stage.

4
TICK-BORNE HUMAN DISEASES

Infections from ticks

Infections only arise if:
- the tick's habitat is invaded at the right season
- the tick is infected
- the human is susceptible to infection
- the human receives an 'infectious dose'

Human disease is the result of a disturbance to normal health and results in an individual developing several complaints (symptoms). This chapter will deal with disease in humans, unless otherwise stated. A tick bite is an injury to the individual. Such an event may result in disease in several ways which can be conveniently classified as early and late effects. There are many precautions which one can take to avoid disease and these will be emphasized in this chapter.

What are the early effects of a tick bite?

Very many individuals will not have any adverse reactions to a tick bite. Initially, the bite is like a small scratch from a rose bush. Afterwards, the most common result of a tick bite is, probably, a local allergic reaction. This is a result of the body's immune system trying to deal with the injury. Various components of the tick, especially its saliva, can act as a stimulus to the immune system and the result is an uncomfortable, red, itchy bite. This is probably the most common tick-borne human disease and the condition usually resolves in a few days. In individuals who are allergic (usually with a history of eczema, asthma or hayfever) there can be a more pronounced reaction to the tick bite. This may manifest as a very large area of affected skin, usually with the development of fluid under the skin forming an uncomfortable area similar to a very severe sunburn. Normally, there is complete healing of the skin, but this may take a few more days. At the same time, the patient may develop several uncomfortable symptoms such as malaise (feeling unwell), nausea, dizziness, headaches and muscle pains. In a very small number of individuals, there is a very severe reaction which is described as an anaphylactic shock: this reaction involves the whole body and may result in the individual becoming unconscious and needing emergency treatment in a hospital.

A local allergic reaction to a tick bite produces mainly itchiness. This can result in the patient, especially young children, vigorously scratching the area. Inevitably, especially with dirty fingernails, such scratching may introduce bacteria into the tick bite. Several bacteria (especially *Staphylococcus aureus* or *Streptococcus pyogenes*) may produce quite severe infections. Even without scratching, the tick bite may become infected. This is because the tick bite produces an area of damaged skin which if rubbed against other objects such as dirty clothes, can result in an infected area. This is especially common in unhygienic living conditions. Fortunately, most of these infections just result in small pustular sores (usually getting better without treatment but occasionally needing antibiotics), and do not have generalised reactions in the body. Occasionally, especially if a large area of skin is involved, the bacterial infections from scratching or clothing will result in serious infection throughout the body and manifest as severe fever, headache, nausea, muscle pains and even unconsciousness. In these individuals, the bacterial infection has been disseminated (spread by the blood), and urgent antibiotic treatment is required.

It is important to be aware that these early effects of tick bites have the potential for development into severe disease. Thus, it is best to remove the tick and then to cover the area with a bandage. This prevents the area from being scratched and also avoids other bacteria getting into the bite.

What are the late effects of a tick bite?

The late effects of a tick bite are due to toxins and infections. Toxins are introduced into the human body by the tick bite and can produce local or disseminated effects. These toxins are not infectious agents themselves but are material produced by the tick which may produce severe disease. Such toxins are distinct from toxins produced by bacteria (from ticks) multiplying in the human body. Fortunately, not very many ticks are able to produce these toxins and such reactions are very rare in Britain. Tick toxins affect animals much more than humans. Symptoms usually appear some days after the tick bite. These toxic reactions have been described all over the world, but especially in tropical countries such as Africa and Australia. There are a variety of symptoms which animals may develop, such as gnashing of teeth, frothy saliva and trembling. In Africa, sweating sickness is very important as it affects many species of animals. Fortunately, a similar reaction in humans is very rare.

Other late effects are tick-borne human infections. Infective agents (see Table 4.1 and 4.2) have been around for a long time and have a complex relationship with their human hosts. Very many infections do not result in any symptoms in humans. Thus, humans will not know that they have been infected unless they have a blood test; such infections are called asymptomatic. The majority of infections probably produce complaints of fever and malaise, often being described as 'flu-like' illnesses. In a minority of infections, there are characteristic symptoms which can identify the infectious agent. The spectrum of symptoms seen with all infections is also present with any one infectious agent. Thus any one infectious agent may result in asymptomatic infection, a flu-like illness or a more characteristic complaint (such as a rash or joint pain).

What are the effects of tick toxins?

Tick paralysis is the most important toxic effect of a tick bite and some 40 species of ticks can produce these toxins. Each year, large numbers of livestock and pets are affected and thousands of animals die as a result of these toxins. Fortunately, humans are very rarely affected and tick paralysis is mainly found in North America and Australia. The condition would probably have to be imported into Britain. There is usually an incubation period of 5-7 days in which there may be symptoms of malaise, nausea and headache. Paralysis of muscles on both sides of the body then follows, usually affecting the lower extremities first and then proceeding up the body. The patient's temperature is usually normal and there are no signs of infection from laboratory tests. When the chest muscles are involved, the patient may die from respiratory failure unless he or she can be adequately treated in an intensive care unit. In North America, the main tick vectors are *Dermacentor andersoni* and *Dermacentor variabilis*. Symptoms may progress for up to a week, but normally progression is more rapid. In very young children, there may be raised temperature and a more acute course with death in 1-2 days. In most cases removal of the attached tick(s) prevents further deterioration and the patient starts to recover completely. This is not the case with the Australian tick, *Ixodes holocyclus*, where removal of the tick can result in a sudden deterioration in the patient's condition. It is believed that the trauma of the removal of the dead tick with damage to blood vessels may result in release of more toxins into the blood stream. In these cases it may be better to kill the tick but to leave the dead tick at the site of attachment. Diagnosis is often dependent on a clinician's awareness of the condition. Two important factors are: the clinical picture of the paralysis and the finding of an engorged tick on the body, often as a result of 5-6 days attachment. Sadly, in many cases the condition is not suspected and the tick is only found after death at a post-mortem examination of the body. Fortunately, this is not a common problem in Britain.

What are the effects of tick infections?

Tick infections can be classified into three main groups according to their causative agent: viruses, bacteria and larger organisms. Every country has its own most common human infectious agents for each main group. The main infectious agents in each group for Britain are in Table 4.1. There are many more infectious agents for the rest of the world, but the ones most likely to be imported into Britain (by individuals having tick bites while abroad) are in Table 4.2. In this chapter, the infectious agents which have been described in Britain will be discussed in greater detail. Obviously, with the ease of jet travel, it is possible for individuals to go on holiday and return with exotic infections to Britain. As these individuals may readily recall a tick bite, the last section of this chapter will briefly discuss the infections in Table 4.2. With all these infections, it is important to remember that infection may not necessarily follow a tick bite or symptoms result from an infection (Chapter 3).

For the infections in this chapter, humans are not an important part of the infectious agent's life cycle. Humans usually get infected because they have wandered into the habitat of the tick. As humans encroach more on forested areas (see Chapter 2), the likelihood of tick bites is increased. In Old Lyme, for example, it was found that new houses which had been built by encroaching on tick-infected areas had high populations of ticks on their lawns.

The exact frequency of the infections in Table 4.1 is not known. Sadly, there are very few large population-studies on

Table 4.1 Tick-borne human diseases in Britain

Organisms	Disease	Frequency	Clinical Effects	Treatment
VIRUSES				
Flavivirus	Louping ill	uncommon	encephalitis	supportive
BACTERIA				
Borrelia burgdorferi	Lyme disease	common	fever skin nervous system joints heart	antibiotics
Coxiella burnetti	Q fever	uncommon	fever heart lungs nervous system	antibiotics
Ehrlichia sennetsu	Ehrlichiosis	not common	fever joints lymph nodes	supportive, occasionally antibiotics
LARGER ORGANISMS				
Babesia spp	Babesiosis	uncommon	fever jaundice anaemia	antibiotics

tick-borne infectious diseases. Nevertheless, the diseases in Table 4.1 will be discussed in order of their perceived frequency and medical importance.

What is Lyme disease?

This is probably the most important tick-borne infection in

Britain. Although there is a greater public and medical awareness of this condition, it is probably still under-recognised.

Occurrence

The occurrence of Lyme disease is related to the distribution and infection in ticks. This world-wide infection is particularly prominent in forested areas in Britain where 5-10% of the human population may have become infected. Places that are exposed and windy, such as tops of mountains, are too hostile for ticks. Infection usually peaks in the months of June and July. Lyme disease is found in patients of all ages but especially in the most active and those most exposed to tick bites. The causative organism is a bacterium called *Borrelia burgdorferi*.

Symptoms

Many patients are asymptomatic and do not know that they have developed the infection. Infection therefore does not necessarily result in disease. The acute disease usually follows 3-32 days after a tick bite. A flu-like illness with fever, malaise, muscle pain, joint pain and a sore throat is common. A characteristic rash (called *erythema chronicum migrans*) is found in some patients (more in North American patients, less in European patients). This rash starts with a raised, red swelling around the tick bite and gradually expands in all directions. The edges of the rash remain red and inflamed whereas there is a central clearing of the rash to produce a characteristic 'target-like lesion' (Figure 4.1). Occasionally, acute disease may also manifest with symptoms of the nervous system involvement such as a stiff neck and photophobia (pain in the eyes on looking at light).

Chronic disease occurs some weeks or months after the acute infection. This may involve :

i) the central nervous system: with a headache, stiff neck and photophobia (this triad of symptoms is due to meningitis). Patients may also be confused, with reduced concentration and

41

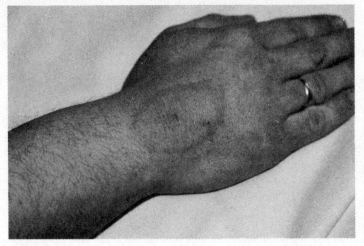

Figure 4.1 Characteristic 'target-like' appearance of *erythema chronicum migrans* rash.

poor memory (usually described as encephalitis). Nerves in the brain (cranial nerves) may be affected and result in facial paralysis (cranial nerve palsies). Involvement of nerves in the rest of the body (peripheral nerves) may result in loss of sensation and tingling of affected areas.

ii) the heart, with chest pain and irregular beats.

iii) joints, with pain and swelling which can seriously limit mobility.

iv) the gastrointestinal tract, resulting in abdominal pain, tenderness and diarrhoea.

v) the liver and spleen, resulting in enlarged organs with tenderness and discomfort.

vi) chronic skin rashes, which are rare and can be difficult to diagnose.

42

Diagnosis

The diagnosis can be made clinically on the characteristic skin rash. In the absence of this rash, diagnosis is more difficult and relies on a clinician's awareness and laboratory tests. There are a variety of tests that can be done on blood samples to identify infection. It is useful to look for antibodies (produced by the body's immune system) against the infectious organisms. Unfortunately, many of these tests may take 3-6 weeks after infection to become positive. Tests may appear falsely negative early in the illness or with antibiotic treatment and may need to be repeated.

Management

The object of management is to kill the organism, to prevent disease progression and to reduce symptoms. Before treatment is started, there must be an assessment of the clinical situation:

i) the risk of infection depends on the length of infected tick attachment: under 24 hours there is little risk; 48 hours, 50% risk; 72 hours, almost certain infection.

ii) infection occurs in about 10% of people bitten by infected ticks, so treatment of all individuals who have been bitten by ticks is not recommended.

iii) characteristic skin rashes must be treated.

iv) chronic disease should be treated, but complete resolution of symptoms may not occur.

v) treatment should be considered in anxious patients who have possible infection.

vi) asymptomatic individuals with positive blood tests probably should not be treated.

Treatment

Treatment must be supervised by a medical practitioner. For early disease, several antibiotics are useful (doxycycline, amoxycillin or ceftriaxone). In patients with penicillin allergies, erythromycin or clarithromycin may be used. For chronic disease, antibiotics should not be given orally but into muscle or blood; drugs of choice are ceftriaxone, cefotaxime or penicillin G.

Prognosis

Despite antibiotic treatment, symptoms recur in 50% of patients although severity and duration are greatly reduced; occasionally recurring symptoms may last several years. Acute disease, cranial nerve palsies and meningitis have a good prognosis. Most central nervous system involvement usually has a favourable outcome; only a few patients have a tendency to chronic or recurrent disease. Joint involvement usually resolves but response may be slow, often needing further treatment. In chronic disease, recurrence is not usual but can occur. Patients may need careful monitoring for months or years depending on the severity of symptoms.

What is Q fever?

The 'Q' here refers to 'query'. This was because when this illness was first described, no-one knew what the causative agent was. This worldwide, common infection of animals, birds and ticks is now known to be caused by the bacterium *Coxiella burnetti*.

Occurrence

Infection usually occurs after inhalation of airborne infected particles of bacteria, especially from excreted material from animals, birds or ticks. Consumption of infected, unpasteurised milk is also a source of infection. A common route of infection is from an infected animal after it has given birth when there is a large infected placenta. Infections as a result of a tick bite are very, very rare. Occupations that are particularly at risk are farmers, abattoir workers and vets.

Symptoms

After an incubation period of 2-3 weeks, many patients are asymptomatic and do not know that they have developed the infection. With patients who have symptoms, there is a wide spectrum of disease from a mild fever to very severe illness with neurological or cardiac involvement. Often there is a sudden onset with chills, headache, weakness and severe sweats. There may be a cough as the lungs can be involved, but more importantly there is disturbance in liver function, and infection of the lungs or heart. A very serious long-term complication is infection of the valves of the heart and in many cases, without appropriate treatment, the individual may require multiple valve replacement operations. Very rarely there is severe neurological disease.

Diagnosis

The diagnosis is made by looking for antibodies to the organism in a sample of blood. These tests may also be used to monitor disease management.

Management

Specific antibiotics can be given for the treatment of the infection, usually tetracyclines or chloramphenicol. Such treatment must be prescribed and monitored by a medical practitioner. In individuals with chronic disease treatment may need to be prolonged. When the heart valves are involved, surgical replacement of these may be required.

Prognosis

Only a very few patients die in the acute phase, usually because they have not been treated. The prognosis is very good for treated individuals who do not develop heart complaints. For the general public, it is important to avoid drinking unpasteurised milk from cows, goats and sheep. There should also be care when handling tissues, especially the placenta from potentially infected animals and other material (hides, skins and animal by-products).

What is Ehrlichiosis?

This is a common illness in dogs, sheep, horses and cattle. Recently, it has been increasingly recognised in humans. It is probably an infection which is reasonably common in Britain, but as the disease is not easily identified, the diagnosis of 'just a viral infection' is usually made. The illness is called sennetsu fever in Japan.

Occurrence

Although ehrlichiosis is a common, world-wide infection of animals, the numbers of human beings that have been infected are unknown. Most cases occur during the spring and summer. In Britain and most of Europe, *Ixodes ricinus*, the sheep tick, is the most involved in the transmission of this infection. The usual causative agent of this tick-borne infection is *Ehrlichia phagocytophilia*, but other members of this group of bacteria are occasionally involved. In different parts of the world, different ticks and *Ehrlichia* species are involved.

Symptoms

In humans, after an incubation period of 1-3 weeks, an asymptomatic infection usually develops. The most characteristic acute presentation is an illness of sudden onset, high fever, headache and nausea. The patient often has very painful muscles and joints. In about a quarter of these patients there is a rash, often a result of bleeding into the skin. Many patients show abnormalities of the bone marrow, with a reduction of white cells (blood cells which especially deal with infection) and platelets (blood components responsible for stopping bleeding). This involvement of the bone marrow is a frequent complication in dogs, and can cause death. Other complaints in animals are extensive weight loss, reduced milk production and among pregnant animals, abortion is common. However, in both humans and animals, this infection is also more likely to present as a non-specific illness with flu-like symptoms. In many cases, the patient may not be ill enough to warrant blood investigations and the precise diagnosis is never made.

Diagnosis

Diagnosis depends on an awareness of the condition among doctors. The presence of a history of tick bites and exposure during the spring or summer with the characteristic symptoms in a particular area of the country should alert the physician. Laboratory examination of the patient's blood can show a reduced white cell and platelet population. In addition, microscopic examination of blood samples may allow the causative organisms to be seen in white cells. Alternatively, patients may have their blood examined by more complicated laboratory tests to detect antibodies.

Management

Objectives of treatment are to correct the abnormalities in the blood, reduce symptoms and to remove bacteria. Appropriate antibiotic treatment will kill the bacteria, and the drug of choice is tetracycline. Patients may also require replacement by blood transfusions of the blood components that are affected, especially to reduce any bleeding. As with other tick-borne infections, prevention of tick bites is an important factor in reducing the number of cases of infected individuals.

What is Babesiosis?

Babesiosis is a very common protozoan infection of animals, but rarely infects humans. Among domestic livestock, especially cattle, there has been a 90% mortality in susceptible herds in the United States of America. Fortunately, the practices of dipping and tick control can dramatically reduce this infection.

Occurrence

Babesiosis shows a similar geographic distribution to Lyme disease, but the epidemic spread of Lyme disease among humans does not appear to occur with babesiosis. In Britain, most infections are probably transmitted by the tick *Ixodes ricinus*; while many in the babesia group of bacteria may be involved, it is mainly *Babesia microti* in Britain. In Europe, most described cases have been in humans who have had their spleen removed (an operation called a splenectomy). This is different from North America where both normal individuals and those with a splenectomy have been affected. It is likely that all humans may be susceptible to this infection, but that it can be more severe if an individual has had a splenectomy.

Symptoms

After a 1-4 week incubation period, a flu-like illness usually develops. The onset may be acute, with extreme fever, malaise, headache, chills, and increased sweating. The infectious agent principally infects red blood cells and this produces destruction of these cells. This is like malaria and the symptoms are similar. The patient has very black urine due to the haemoglobin from the destroyed red cells, and there can be a resultant anaemia (reduced haemoglobin in the blood). The fever comes and goes but does not have the same pattern as malaria. Like malaria, the parasite may persist for several months, and chronic conditions such as cirrhosis of the liver may develop. Illness may resolve in a few weeks or may last many months or years.

Diagnosis

Blood is usually examined as for malaria infection, and the diagnosis is made by seeing the babesia micro-organism with a microscope. Unfortunately, this can be difficult when there are few organisms in the blood. Tests may need to be repeated. It may also be useful to look for antibodies.

Treatment

Treatment for babesiosis is difficult as none of the antibiotics appear to have very great activity against the organism. Fortunately, in many cases only supportive treatment (to alleviate symptoms) is required, especially blood transfusions. However, in severe cases, drugs used for malaria (chloroquine, quinine and pyrimethamine) can be used. Clindamycin has also been shown to be effective.

Prognosis

In most cases the individual makes a complete recovery. A few cases are fatal with a rapid progression of disease, especially in those with splenectomy. Occasionally the illness becomes chronic.

What is louping ill?

Louping ill disease of animals has been recognised for many centuries. The name comes from the old Scots word 'loup' which was used to describe the effect in sheep of an infection of the brain (encephalitis) which caused the sheep to 'spring into the air'. Although the first human case was described in 1934, the disease seems to have become less common in the last decades.

Occurrence

Occurrence of louping ill depends on the presence of ticks which transmit infection. In Britain this is *Ixodes ricinus*. The infection is particularly prevalent in areas where there are many sheep, especially on rough grazing and hill pastures. In Britain, human infection is particularly prevalent in Northern Scotland, the Western Isles, North Wales, Northern England and in Ireland. Humans who have close association with animals are particularly affected. Farmers, butchers, abattoir workers, vets and laboratory workers have an increased risk of developing this infection.

Symptoms

After an incubation period of 3-7 days, the infection develops. In many cases it is asymptomatic. In a large number of cases, the symptoms are of a flu-like illness with high fever, headache, malaise, anorexia, dizziness, muscle and joint pain. The most characteristic presentation is of an illness with two phases. The first phase is a fever with flu-like symptoms. Then, there is a short period of improvement and the patient feels better. This is followed by the second phase of severe neurological involvement, characterised by high fever, meningitis (severe headache, photophobia and neck stiffness), tremors of the head and limbs, vomiting, and paralysis. The paralysis may be as in poliomyelitis, especially with the limbs being involved.

Diagnosis

The diagnosis is usually made by the clinical presentation and the history of a tick bite. Again, an increased awareness of the condition by the physician is critical in making an early diagnosis. Confirmation of the diagnosis is by examination of blood samples for antibodies to the louping ill virus. Antibodies may take several weeks to develop and several blood samples may have to be taken.

Management

For most cases, management is confined to treatment of the symptoms and providing support for the patient. In a very few cases, especially when the symptoms involve the nervous system (meningitis, encephalitis, or poliomyelitis-like symptoms) the patient may require admission to hospital. In hospital, the patient can be given support whilst the viral infection runs its course. There is no specific treatment to kill the virus.

Prognosis

Fortunately, the vast majority of patients have a mild illness after which there is complete recovery. In a few individuals, the illness involves the central nervous system and then the recovery may be prolonged. In some cases, convalescence may last years and the patient can suffer recurrence of central nervous system symptoms.

What are the other worldwide viral infections?

Throughout the world there are numerous viral infections which can be transmitted by tick bites. As the list probably runs into hundreds of viral infections, only the important ones will be discussed in this chapter. The main viruses are as in Table 4.2. Nevertheless, it should be remembered that in any one country in the world, their own tick-borne viral infection will be more important. In this chapter, the importance of an infection is its likelihood of being imported into Britain by individuals being infected abroad, either on a short holiday or from working abroad.

Occurrence
Outbreaks of each infection will depend on the tick life cycle. This will be dependent on which part of the world is being visited. In addition, an individual tick may have a different seasonal peak in different countries, dependent on the weather. As can be seen by Table 4.2, most infections are due to particular types of virus called flaviviruses or nairoviruses.

Symptoms
After an incubation period of 1-2 weeks, a number of patients will develop an asymptomatic infection. Of those who develop a symptomatic infection, there are three main clinical presentations:

1. An acute illness involving the central nervous system, with meningitis or encephalitis leading to paralysis, coma and death. Such fatal illnesses are, fortunately, not common.

2. An acute onset with fever, occasionally with a rash, and less commonly with central nervous system involvement.

Table 4.2 Other world-wide tick-borne human diseases

Organism	Disease	Occurrence	Clinical Features
VIRUSES			
Flavivirus	Tick-borne encephalitis	Europe, Asia	encephalitis paralysis
Flavivirus	Powassan encephalitis	Canada USA, Russia	encephalitis
Flavivirus	Omsk haemorrhagic fever	Russia	bleeding fever
Flavivirus	Kyasanur Forest disease	India	bleeding, fever meningitis encephalitis
Nairovirus	Nairobi sheep disease	Africa, India	fever
Nairovirus	Crimean-Congo haemorrhagic fever	Europe, Africa Asia, Middle East	bleeding fever
Orbivirus	Colorado tick fever	USA, Canada	fever
BACTERIA			
Rickettsia rickettsii	Rocky Mountain spotted fever	North and South America	bleeding fever, rash
Rickettsia conorii	Boutonneuse fever (Mediterranean spotted fever)	Africa, Asia India, Europe	fever, rash
Rickettsia sibirica	North Asian tick typhus	Siberia, Asia Mongolia Eastern Europe	rash, fever
Borrelia recurrentis	Relapsing fever	Asia, Africa South America North America	relapsing fever
Francisella tularensis	Tularaemia	North America Mexico, Europe China, Japan	ulcer, eyes enlarged glands abdomen

3. An acute onset of fever and bleeding (haemorrhagic fever). As bleeding may be internal or external, the patient is seriously ill and fatalities may be high.

Diagnosis

The diagnosis is usually made by the characteristic symptoms in the patient, and an awareness of the infection in the particular area in which the patient has resided or visited. Evidence of the infection may take some time to develop, but antibodies to the viral infection can usually be detected in the blood 2-3 weeks after the tick bite.

Treatment

For a vast majority of patients who become infected, no specific treatment is required. In those that have central nervous system involvement, admission to hospital is required if symptoms are severe. Supportive treatment to reduce symptoms is given. There are no specific anti-viral drugs that can be used against these infections. In individuals in which there is bleeding, blood trans-fusion or transfusion of other blood products may be required.

Prognosis

Although in a small number of patients infection may be fatal, in the majority of those infected there is a favourable outcome. In those individuals who have central nervous system involvement, complete recovery may take many months or, more rarely, years. It is thus critical that patients be aware of the possibilities of infection and take adequate precautions to reduce tick bites.

What are the other world-wide bacterial infections?

As can be seen from Table 4.2, the bacterial infections which can be transmitted by tick bites occur throughout the world. An infection may occur in countries with different climatic conditions, or may be restricted to particular areas of the world. As with viral infections, the list in Table 4.2 emphasises infections which may be imported into Britain; a complete list of world-wide tick-borne bacterial infections would run to many pages! Again, it is important to emphasise that individuals returning from a particular country, especially if their lifestyle allowed many tick bites, should seek medical advice about what are the most important tick-borne infections from that country rather than depend on the completeness of Table 4.2.

Occurrence

As throughout this chapter, infection depends on the season and the likelihood of tick bites. Infections with a world-wide presentation will have different peaks of activity in different countries dependent on the local weather conditions. The widespread distribution of the infections stated in Table 4.2 shows the great success of these bacterial agents in managing to survive in parts of the world with quite different climatic conditions.

Symptoms

After an incubation period of 1-14 days, most patients will develop an asymptomatic infection. When symptoms are present, there are three characteristic clinical presentations:

1. An acute illness, with fever and a rash. A rash is usually manifest as redness of the skin. In some cases (for example Rocky Mountain spotted fever), there is also bleeding into the skin (haemorrhagic fever).

2. An acute illness with relapsing fever. Periods of fever last 2-9 days and alternate with periods without fever lasting 2-4 days. The number of relapses may vary from 1-10 or more. Each period of fever is characterised by rising temperature and finishes with a shaking chill and profuse sweating. The causative agent of this presentation is mainly *Borrelia recurrentis*.

3. An illness called tularaemia (also known as rabbit fever,

deer-fly fever, Francis disease) which is usually manifest as skin ulcers. There may be involvement of the eyes, enlarged lymph nodes, and abdominal complaints (pain, diarrhoea and vomiting). The causative organism is *Francisella tularensis.*

Diagnosis

The characteristic symptoms in a patient, a history of tick bite, and a knowledge of infections in the country visited are important clues to the diagnosis. Evidence of infection may take some time to develop, but antibodies to the particular bacterial infection can usually be detected in the blood 2-3 weeks after the tick bite. In some cases, it may be possible to grow the bacteria in special laboratory conditions.

Treatment

For many patients, no specific treatment is required. In those that have a more severe illness, specific antibiotic treatment is available, but should only be administered under medical supervision. In individuals with severe bleeding, hospital admission may be required and the individual may require blood transfusion or transfusion of other blood products to stop bleeding.

Prognosis

The majority of those infected will have a favourable outcome. When bleeding is severe, especially if the liver is involved, fatalities may result. Early antibiotic treatment is associated with a very favourable outcome, and hospital admission is critical for speedy diagnosis and management.

5

A REALISTIC APPROACH TO TICK INFECTIONS

Lyme disease symptoms
(Many people will have no symptoms)

- Flu-like illness: malaise, fever, aches
- Skin rash ('target-like' appearances)
- Joint pain and swelling
- Nervous system involvement, especially brain and loss of sensation with tingling in other nerves in the body
- Chest pains and irregular heart beats

It is difficult for the general public to have sufficient information and knowledge to develop a realistic approach to many infections. Matters are also often made worse by the media, politicians and self-interested groups. Thus, whether it is salmonella infection in eggs or bovine spongieform encephalopathy (BSE) in meat, it is difficult to know what to do for the best. Often, medical advice on best practice may change with fashion: butter being 'bad' for you, then 'good' for you. Similarly, one is told to avoid alcohol and then that a little red wine is good for you. Indeed, one can get the impression that the medical profession is as confused as the rest of the population in terms of giving good advice!

The main difficulty for the general public is understanding 'risk'. To most individuals, risk is something that can really cause harm. However, in the medical use of the word: 'the risk associated with some potentially harmful factor is defined as the proportion who become ill out of all those exposed to it.' Therefore, it is not definitely the case that the harmful factor always causes disease. Thus, a tick bite is a harmful factor but does not necessarily cause disease.

A further complication is the use of the word 'exposed'. To the general public, if you have been exposed to something, there are inevitable consequences. Thus, if you are exposed to rain, you get wet. Unfortunately with infections it is not as straightforward. If you are exposed to an infection, you do not necessarily become infected. Further, if you do become infected, you may not develop a disease (a state of ill-health) as many who become infected are asymptomatic (have normal health with no complaints). The object of this chapter is to provide information in such a way that the reader may be able to apply the knowledge to his/her particular situation.

How do you become infected?

Large numbers of people will visit areas where there are ticks and where many ticks are infected. Many people live in areas with a high population of ticks. Nevertheless, only a very small number of individuals will become infected. It is really quite difficult to become infected. This fact should reassure most individuals and allow them to enjoy a particular place without undue worry over infections. Further, an informed individual can take appropriate precautions to avoid tick bites and so further reduce the risks of infection.

As explained in Chapter 3, infection depends on the interaction of several factors: the tick, the habitat and the human being. Firstly, as the tick needs to be infected with a particular organism and the majority of ticks are not infected, most ticks cannot transmit infection. The habitat must be conducive to tick survival or else those ticks that are infected will die out. Lastly, the human being needs to be susceptible to that infection. If any of these conditions are not satisfied, there will be no risks of infection to the human being. Even in cases where these conditions are satisfied, infection will only occur if the human has received a sufficiently large infectious dose (Chapter 3). If there is an insufficient infectious dose, there will be no infection. Simply visiting an area with infected ticks is insufficient for one to worry about receiving an infection. Indeed, even if one has had several tick bites, it is not inevitable that one will become infected. Even if one lived in an area where tick bites were a part of life, the majority of the population in that area will not become infected.

As described in Chapter 4, even when there is infection, the results depend on several factors, especially the human's immune system. Of those infected, the vast majority will have an asymptomatic infection; thus, the results of most infections will not be discernible to the individual. Others who are infected will have non-specific symptoms, such as fever, malaise or having a flu-like illness. In only a very few individuals will there be a characteristic illness such as distinctive rashes. For all of these tick-borne infections, the human being is not the primary target. It is important for those visiting and those living in areas with ticks to recognise this fact and not have undue concerns.

Are risks equal?

Many people believe that the risks of getting any infection are equal. This is incorrect. All infectious agents differ in infectiveness, so some organisms are very infectious whereas others are not. This is also compatible with most people's experiences of infections: some infections quickly infect everyone within a family, whereas others may only infect one or two individuals. This difference in those affected is termed an organism's infectiveness, and determines your likelihood of developing a particular infection.

For a tick to transmit an infection to humans, the tick must first have been infected from feeding on other animals. Less commonly, a tick may become infected from a human and transmit an infection to another human. Thus, if large numbers of animals are infected, it seems more likely that human beings will become infected. However, certain infections are very common in animals, but do not necessarily infect ticks to the same extent. Similarly, some infections are very common in animals and ticks, but are uncommon in humans. The explanation is that infectious agents may not easily cross the species' barrier (animals to ticks or ticks to humans). Consideration of the infectiveness of an organism and its ability to cross the species' barrier shows that the risks of developing different infections are not equal. Therefore, in Table 4.1 (Chapter 4), the protozoan *Babesia spp* can produce high infection rates in animals and ticks, but not in humans. Conversely, the bacterium *Borrelia burgdorferi* probably infects animals, ticks and humans to a similar extent. For an individual visiting a tick-infected area for these two diseases, there is a great chance of developing *Borrelia burgdorferi* infection, but a much smaller chance of developing babesiosis.

Are all infections the same?

For many people, if they develop an infection it is bad news. It is commonly perceived that all infections are the same. As was seen in Chapter 4 (Table 4.1), all infections are quite different in terms of their infectiveness. An infection's importance is usually related to its clinical presentation and the severity of infection. Therefore, Lyme disease is a common infection but is not usually severe in its early disease presentation. In comparison, louping ill is a very uncommon infection, but is very severe in its presentation of an acute illness with encephalitis. For infections such as ehrlichiosis and Lyme disease, there are a large number of individuals who have an asymptomatic infection or an infection with a non-specific illness. This is not seen with infections such as louping ill, Q fever and babesiosis. These latter illnesses do not frequently present with an asymptomatic infection or non-specific clinical findings.

If an individual is visiting a particular area of a country, it is useful to know which infection is likely to be in that place. For individuals who reside in tick-infested areas, there is often local knowledge of places with high tick populations and even if there are particular high risks of infection. This knowledge can be usefully combined with how common the infection is and the usual clinical features of the infection (Chapter 4). It would be an interesting—but sadly insoluble—philosophical question to know which is better: to risk an infection which is very common but whose clinical presentation may not be very severe, or an infection which is uncommon with a more severe clinical presentation.

If one considers the infectiveness, frequency and clinical presentation of an infectious agent, it is possible to draw several conclusions. Firstly, most infectious organisms do not usually produce very severe clinical presentations in the majority of individuals. Secondly, the infectious agents that have a very severe clinical presentation are usually not as infectious or as common. However, a difficulty with general statements is that they are quite useful in determining your overall outlook, but are not useful in a particular case. Therefore, if you know that an infection occurs in 1 in 100 patients and another infection occurs in 1 in 100,000 patients, you can say that you are less worried about the latter infection. This would be quite an objective assessment, but it would not be appropriate if you happen to be the one individual involved! If you are the one individual with a very uncommon, severe infection it does not really matter if this state is common or rare.

In conclusion, all infections are not the same, and differ dramatically in their frequency and clinical presentations. Medical practitioners are aware of the importance of different infections, but it can be difficult for the general public to have a similar approach. Simply, one should be particularly worried about certain infections but much less so about others.

Are infection risks greater abroad?

Frequent travel abroad is now a common feature of life for very many individuals. Many perceive that travel abroad is associated with greater infection risks. This perception is partly true: there are more infections in tropical countries compared to temperate countries and there are more infections in developing countries compared to developed countries. Since many holidays are in tropical and developing countries, there is a greater risk of infection to the traveller. In addition, many individuals travelling to foreign countries would not have been exposed to very many of the indigenous infections; with reduced immunity, the risk of becoming ill is greater. Therefore, for those travelling abroad, this is the time when there is a greater exposure to infections and the likelihood of becoming infected is higher than remaining in Britain.

For tick-borne infections, the risks of travel abroad are only greater if there is a higher exposure to ticks. This exposure depends on the type of holiday. Obviously, individuals who are trekking in forests have considerably greater risks than individuals who are lying on the beach. Activity holidays are therefore a greater risk than the beach/bar/nightclub holiday. Similarly, in this country, individuals who are in towns and cities are at much smaller risk than those who are camping or in rural surroundings. For most individuals going to beach-type holidays, the risks of tick-borne infection are very low.

Important considerations are also the time of year that the holiday is planned; for example the time of peak tick activity has greater risk. The accommodation is also a significant factor. Most package holidays in good hotels represent very little risk. On the other hand, individuals who are backpacking, camping or sleeping rough are at considerably greater risk. In planning a holiday, it is quite important to know what infections might be at their peak in the particular country to be visited. As can be seen in

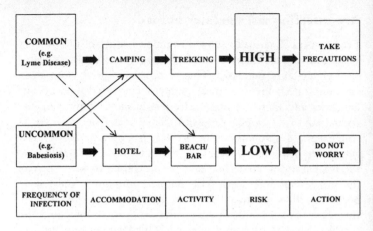

Figure 5.1 Influence of several factors on risk of infection and appropriate action

Table 4.2 (Chapter 4), there are very many serious infections which may be acquired whilst travelling abroad. Nevertheless, this information is usually available from the travel agent and the modern traveller is much more informed than those who went abroad several decades ago.

A recent report has shown that up to 30% of travellers will become ill whilst on holiday. The vast majority of these illnesses are related to the gastro-intestinal tract. In many cases, it is also difficult to separate true infections from over-indulgence in alcohol. In comparison to these risks, the risk of tick-borne infections is very remote. Whilst it is acceptable for an individual on a beach/bar holiday to have little knowledge of tick-borne infections, the same cannot be said for an individual trekking in forests, sleeping rough or camping (Figure 5.1). For those in the latter group, there should be a clear understanding that infection risks are substantial and that appropriate precautions should be taken to avoid tick bites.

What is a realistic approach to tick infection?

A common problem for many individuals is that knowledge of illnesses can create more anxiety than benefits. In this book, it is hoped that a realistic approach to tick-borne infections can be developed. However, this depends on an individual being able to apply knowledge to his/her situation. Application of knowledge can be very difficult, but is critical in demonstrating a true understanding of the subject. In Figure 5.1, two infections in Britain (Lyme disease and babesiosis) are taken as examples of how other factors may influence the risk of developing an infection. When one knows if the risk of developing an infection is high or low, then the most appropriate course of action can be taken.

For individuals who live in areas of high tick populations, a realistic approach to infection is more difficult; often, by the nature of their employment, such as dealing with animals, or from having domestic pets, it is difficult to avoid tick bites. Fortunately the evidence is that in those who have such repeated exposure to tick bites infection is not common, probably as a result of acquired immunity. Infection risks can also be reduced by sticking to established pathways, especially at times of the year of peak tick activity. There may also be local knowledge that a particular area is associated with some infections. For those living in rural areas, there has always been the need to develop an understanding of nature, of which tick bites and infection are a small part.

As stated in Figure 5.1, those individuals that are at higher risk should take appropriate precautions. The precautions that one can take to avoid tick bites are described in Chapter 6. Many individuals are very reassured by this knowledge and can be meticulous about taking precautions. Unfortunately, it should always be remembered that precautions only reduce the risks of infection and do not prevent infection. The concept of no infection only exists for an individual who is living in a plastic bubble.

For any individual who is exposed to normal living conditions, there is always a small risk of infection.

It is therefore possible for somebody with high risks of infection who takes all appropriate precautions to reduce his/her risks of infection to something approaching the levels of those individuals who have a low risk of developing infections. However, in Figure 5.1, the appropriate action for individuals with low risks of infection is: 'do not worry'. It therefore seems that the same advice can be given to individuals with low risk of infection and to those individuals who have a high risk of infection but who take appropriate precautions. Is this sensible ? The answer is yes. Another major consideration is that individuals who worry about illnesses or about the possibilities of infection can affect the outcome of infection. Undue concern or worry can by itself depress the functioning of the immune system and therefore increase the possibility of infection. Therefore, an individual who has a depressed immune system as a result of undue anxiety, concern, or worry will be susceptible to a smaller infectious dose of an organism compared to an individual who is less worried. The message is clear: if the circumstances dictate that one is at high risk, one should take appropriate precautions but should not be particularly worried. Similarly, if one is at low risk one should not worry. It would be particularly sad if the appropriate actions are taken by an individual, but because of undue anxiety and worry, the fear of developing an infection is realised.

Before the consequences of infections can be properly assessed, it is important to understand that the risks of infection need to be balanced against the pleasure of the activity. Trekking in forests or camping in woodlands are pleasurable activities, and individuals who undertake these activities do so because the activities are associated with great happiness. For this happiness, they are prepared to suffer discomforts (such as a lack of washing or toilet facilities). The experience of being close to nature and away from all the trappings of civilised life can produce great happiness. Therefore, to develop a realistic approach to tick-borne infections, the great pleasure and satisfaction that results from a particular activity and lifestyle must be balanced by the possibility of illness. It is similar to the great pleasure that is experienced from having a late night take-away, although it is well recognised that such indulgence may result in an attack of gastro-intestinal disturbance!

6
THE CONTROL OF TICKS ON HUMANS

Tick control

- Worldwide, after a century of pesticide applications, few ticks have been successfully eradicated.
- What drives tick control is the needs of farming. Human health comes second.
- The most effective way to control human infections from ticks is through health education.
- The use of tick repellents is helpful but is no substitute for the daily tick inspection.
- The use of pesticides, the eradication of wildlife hosts or alteration of tick habitats may be useful in localized situations.

The size of the problem

Few parasites have proved as difficult to eradicate as ticks. Control, let alone eradication, of ticks is a formidable task. Unlike most blood-sucking insect pests, ticks are immensely reproductive, remarkably long-lived and can survive starvation for long periods. Attempts to blitz ticks by aerial spraying of pesticides comes up against a further problem—ticks are widely dispersed in forests, pastures and moors and spend most of the year sheltering, resting, moulting or laying eggs in cracks and crevices in the soil or at the base of dense vegetation, largely beyond reach of pesticides. In addition, there is no pesticide which specifically targets ticks—the pesticides marketed against ticks are lethal to spiders as well as to insects and other invertebrates.

The fact remains that after a century of throwing pesticide after pesticide at the problem, few ticks have been successfully eradicated for long periods and then only in limited localities.

Ticks, like insects, may in time acquire resistance to pesticides. And even where tick numbers are brought under control, relaxation of the control frequently results in a new infestation from neighbouring untreated areas.

There is another problem—the fight against ticks, worldwide, is driven primarily by the needs of farming. Undoubtedly, human health has benefited, but this has been largely a by-product of the prior claims of animal health. There are exceptions; in areas such as southern Germany, Switzerland and the eastern USA public concern over human Lyme disease has encouraged the public health authorities to look for inspiration from the agro-chemical and animal health industry.

The solutions

Of all the available approaches to controlling human infections from ticks, the ones which have been of particular benefit are these:

> *Health education*
> *Tick repellents*
> *Pesticides*
> *Habitat modification*
> *Host eradication*

Each approach has its merits and drawbacks.

Health education

Public awareness of ticks and tick–borne diseases has developed considerably in recent years largely as a result of Lyme disease. In Britain, the lead for this has been the feature articles and commentaries published in newspapers and some of the magazines for walkers, climbers, campers and naturalists. These articles warn readers of the dangers of tick-borne diseases and offer advice on how to recognize and remove a feeding tick.

Advice on ticks and human health also appears from time to

time in the farming, forestry and shooting press. The rural industries of farming, shepherding, crofting, gamekeeping and stalking are occasionally targeted by one of the Government departments through bulletins and other publications of limited circulation. And for several years, warnings and advice on ticks have been issued to field workers employed by the Government's environmental agencies such as English Nature or Scottish Natural Heritage and to university-based field scientists contracted to the Natural Environment Research Council. However, for the majority of people, particularly those seeking an innocent day out in the country, ticks are an unexpected, unseen and often unheeded hazard.

Over recent decades, a very real expectation has developed among holiday-makers, especially those from urban areas, that countryside excursions should be safe and not a health hazard, neither to themselves nor to their children. In Britain, this group, several million strong, attracted to the countryside to seek their well-earned recreation, will miss out on advice on ticks. At best, some will read the occasional articles in the broadsheet press on ticks and Lyme disease, but they may be the lucky ones. The north American approach has been very different. The walker or camper in say Connecticut or Massachusetts has access to free fact sheets on Lyme disease issued by the state health services. Game hunters in Canada and through much of the eastern USA are targeted by tick-repellent manufacturers with leaflets on ticks and tick recognition. For those with specific concerns, information packs are available published by health charities such as the Lyme Disease Foundation. Or the armchair tourist can access the Lyme Disease National Hotline by phone, fax or through the Internet. In Britain, however, endeavours to improve public awareness of ticks and tick-borne diseases are, by comparison, relatively undeveloped.

Repellents

Undoubtedly the best way to acquire ticks is to stroll through sheep- or deer-grazed grassland at the right season stark naked or at least with legs bared. For those with a taste for it, the kilt is ideal, with or without a crummock in the hand! Combine this with a little sweat and heavy breathing and ticks will come scuttling. It follows then that the best anti-tick repellent is the solid barrier of clothing—sealed boots, trouser legs tucked into boots or socks drawn over trousers and the wearing of long-sleeved shirts. Really determined pin-head sized nymphs, however, will do all they can to find a chink in the clothing barrier, so a thorough daily inspection of one's person may still be needed. However, the combination of a good clothing cover and a daily skin inspection should mean there is no need to resort to repellents.

However, the chemical option is there. The idea is that the chemical repellent applied directly to the skin or to clothing should discourage, preferably ward off, the insect or tick from settling on the skin. The most widely available anti-tick repellent is DEET (diethyl toluamide) usually marketed as an insect repellent against midges and mosquitoes. When applied to clothing, typically socks and trouser legs, it is fairly effective against ticks and in at least one field trial achieved an 80% reduction in tick bites.

In terms of safety, DEET has been around for fifty years and there is no substantial body of evidence that it is harmful to adults when applied directly to the skin, occasionally and in small quantities. However, DEET, like most repellents absorbed by the skin, passes through the liver before being excreted some hours later. *Its use on children is not recommended.* Where there is an option it would seem sensible to apply DEET to clothing rather than to the skin—but not, absolutely not, to nylon-based clothing which many repellents will dissolve.

Permethrin is also marketed as a tick-repellent, though strictly, rather than repelling, it actually kills the tick (and many other invertebrates) on contact. This is a powerful synthetic version of the pyrethroids, natural insecticides found in relatives of the chrysanthemum family. A Permethrin-based clothing spray is available from the USA where, it should be noted, its use directly on the skin is *not* authorized. However, both DEET- and Permethrin-impregnated clothing quickly lose their anti-tick properties and the treatment may need to be repeated daily for maximum effect. A number of other tick repellents are sold which double up as insect repellents. None have been outstandingly successful.

Each year attractively packaged balms, potions and elixirs are sold, usually pleasantly scented, and claiming to ward off ticks and insects. This is a potentially lucrative market but most of these medicaments do not seem to survive the hard test of consumer approval. There is a fortune to be made if an effective, risk-free, tick-repellent were to be marketed. But it has not happened yet.

Pesticides

Why not eradicate ticks through pesticides? Pesticides are widely used to protect humans from the ravages of insect-borne diseases, particularly in the tropics. The military operational problems posed by malaria in World War II led directly to the widespread use of DDT, specifically to combat malaria-carrying mosquitoes. During the late 1940s through to the early 1960s DDT and other chlorinated hydrocarbons were widely employed in the war against mosquitoes, tse-tse flies, black flies, lice and other insects implicated in human diseases. The pesticide campaigns often involved aerial spraying over considerable areas and undoubtedly brought relief to millions of people. The same campaigns, however, proved a disaster to wildlife.

It is a hard fact of life that within a few years of its widespread application, insects sooner or later will develop resistance to a pesticide. This happened with DDT by the early 1950s. Ticks too have developed resistance to pesticides. Today we have ticks which are resistant to pyrethroids and organophosphates. This, of course, is what keeps the pesticide industry in business.

Anti-tick pesticides are widely used to control ticks on live-stock (see Chapter 7) and any direct benefits to human health are usually incidental. The reason that pesticides are not targeted against ticks solely for the benefit of human health is that humans are not the main target of the tick, but form, at best, an occasional opportunity to secure a blood meal. This may be no succour to the hill walker or forester who subsequently contracts Lyme disease. Anti-tick pesticides have been used as part of a (human) public health campaign in localized hot-spots for Lyme disease, especially in recreational areas, near built-up areas and on military bases, mainly in the USA. However, the considerable environmental risk and public resistance to broad-scale spraying makes this approach limited in its application.

Habitat modification

Perhaps the most widespread method of controlling ticks is to modify the natural environment. Targeted habitats include the areas around recreation parks and camp sites. Habitat modification usually involves altering the form and composition of vegetation by mowing, burning, through herbicides and by clearance of scrub and trees. The principle is simple enough—to create a habitat which does not offer ticks a sanctuary to lay eggs, to rest, to over-winter, to allow questing or to secure a blood meal. The ultimate tick-unfriendly habitat would be a large area covered in concrete and free of livestock, small mammals and all plant life—a city centre car park, for example.

On a local scale, undoubtedly habitat modification does work. The approach has been widely applied in residential areas on the edges of towns and villages, particularly in North America where there is public concern over the presence of Lyme disease-carrying ticks. Often the approach used is to alter the habitat to discourage deer and other mammals. Typically, on the outskirts of residential areas or the edges of camp sites, encroaching wood-land is cut down with regular mowing of vegetation alongside footpaths. The trouble is that vegetation does not stand still and the habitat management regime needs to be kept going each and every year. Small mammals, notoriously, will often rapidly recolonize areas, particularly after burning and mowing, bringing in their own fresh complement of ticks.

Host eradication

Another approach is not to tackle the tick itself but to deal with the tick's food source—the principle being that if the tick is deprived of a blood meal for long enough it will die of starvation. Putting the principle into practice has been the aim of host eradication campaigns for many decades.

Many observations have confirmed that where there is a high density of hosts—deer, sheep, cattle, field mice and so on, there tends to be a large number of ticks. The introduction of large flocks of sheep into the Scottish Highlands in the nineteenth century brought with it the tick-borne disease louping-ill and anecdotal evidence of a large increase in tick-infested pastures. In the USA a number of attempts have been made to reduce the incidence of Lyme disease by reducing deer herd sizes. However, trials in Cape Cod, bounded on three sides by the Atlantic, only achieved a significant reduction in Lyme disease when almost all of the deer had been eliminated. Indeed, there was some evidence that as the number of deer declined so hungry ticks began plaguing humans. In another Massachusetts experiment, this time on an off-shore island, all of the resident tick-infested white-tailed deer were shot in an attempt to eradicate Lyme disease. Unhappily, the adult ticks, deprived of their deer, simply moved to racoons. Perhaps then the racoons could have been eliminated, but where do you stop?

In recreational areas in parts of Germany, Austria and Switzerland deer fences have been erected specifically in an attempt to reduce the incidence of Lyme disease by excluding deer. The approach has limited application and may backfire, particularly when the original attraction of the area for visitors was the very sight of deer!

Anti-tick measures against livestock may be far more effective than attempts to control ticks on wildlife, though not always. Lax veterinary controls have seen the spread of tick-borne diseases into Europe. The origin of tick-borne human encephalitis in western Europe is believed to have been the movement of cattle from eastern Europe. Mediterranean spotted fever appears to have spread northwards on the backs of tick-infested dogs. The vets cannot be blamed, however, for the spread of human haemorrhagic fever from Ukraine. This fever is thought to have spread to western Europe through infected ticks on hares and migratory birds.

The way forward

For most people ticks and tick-borne diseases are a relatively new phenomenon. After all, the increasingly familiar name 'Lyme disease' was only coined a little more than twenty years ago. In Britain, publicity in newspapers and particularly the farming and hill walking press has done something to improve awareness of ticks. In time the public health authorities may add their weight to education campaigns. But for the immediate future, it is almost certain that we humans will have to remain content with the hard fact that the control of ticks in Britain, as in much of the rest of the world, is in the hands of those concerned primarily with animal health. Short of a major epidemic, it is unlikely that limited public health resources will be diverted to protecting humans from ticks.

The way forward would seem to be not with repellents or pesticides, nor with large scale habitat modification. Recent changes, or forecasts of change, in the scale and form of livestock farming could well influence the size of the tick population on pasture land and rough grazing. The expansion of forested areas and the exclusion of red deer from large areas of the Scottish Highlands will be watched with interest. Changes in climate, particularly rainfall and temperature, are likely to affect the questing and biting behaviour of our resident tick populations, particularly so the sheep-tick with its distinct patterns of seasonal activity. All of these changes will have an effect on the incidence of ticks biting humans and inevitably on tick-borne disease.

Until we know more about the changes in patterns of tick activity and the incidence of tick-borne diseases in Britain, for the foreseeable future there will be no substitute for education—authoritative practical information on ticks and tick-borne diseases and how to avoid them—not just a health warning for the serious hill walker, climber, shooter, fisher, farmer, crofter or forester, but for all who seek no more than a healthy and rewarding walk in the countryside.

And if all else fails—what to do if a tick bites!

How to remove a tick

- Ticks should be removed from the body promptly but, more important, correctly.
- Use tweezers not finger nails.
- Lay the tweezers firmly on the skin close to the tick's mouth parts.
- Grasp the tick and pull it out steadily without twisting.
- Clean up the wound.
- Watch the wound over subsequent days.

At the end of the day, despite repellents and pesticides, if a tick bites it must be removed! For the reasons given in previous chapters the risk of infection can be reduced significantly if the tick is removed *promptly*. The procedure, which is exactly the same for both pets and people, is simple and effective provided three key points are borne in mind.

1. The tick has a pair of barbed headpieces which are firmly anchored into the wound during feeding. In addition, the tick secretes a cement-like substance which binds the head firmly to the wound. The result is that ticks are more likely to break up if improperly handled, so leaving the head-part embedded in the skin.

2. Ticks can be readily removed at home or in the field and it is *not* necessary to call out the doctor! People who work with animals or pursue rural occupations in tick-infested areas are well used to removing ticks.

3. A most important point, the tick should be removed *completely* and parts of the headpiece should *not* be left in the flesh. Complete removal is usually not difficult. All that is needed is a pair of tweezers—preferably fine-pointed straight tweezers.

The tip of the tweezers should be placed on either side of the tick's mouth parts (the place where the tick is attached to the skin) laying the tweezers *as close to the skin as possible*. Gently but firmly close the tweezers and—steadily—pull the tick straight out. It is quite unnecessary to twist while pulling—indeed twisting the tick out is one way of breaking off the barbed headpiece and leaving it in the flesh.

If a pair of tweezers is not immediately available it is better to wait and remove the tick later that day. Attempting to remove a tick with finger nails should be avoided—but if it has to be done then use a paper tissue or clean handkerchief to avoid contact with potentially infected tick fluids. If parts of the head are left in the wound a thorough attempt should be made to extract the pieces in the same way as a splinter would be removed, using tweezers or, if necessary, a sterilized needle. Having removed the tick, the wound should be cleaned with an antiseptic cream, or alcohol, the tweezers disinfected and the hands washed thoroughly with soap and water.

Do *not* prick out, crush or burn the tick as this may cause the tick to release its fluids into the wound, possibly under pressure. And do not attempt to swathe or smother the tick in creams, ointments, soap, petroleum jelly, whisky, nail varnish or other liquids. Ticks are most unlikely to release their hold on the flesh, particularly if they have been attached for some hours.

Children should *not* be encouraged to pull out ticks but should always seek help from an adult. Keep an eye on the tick bite over the following days. The area around the bite may redden for a few days but this should soon clear up. If it does not clear up go to your doctor. Finally, there is no substitute for vigilance. A daily inspection for ticks during the tick season should be a routine practice.

7
TICKS—THEIR IMPACT ON LIVESTOCK AND WILDLIFE

Effects of tick-borne diseases

- Epidemics of tick-borne diseases of livestock can destroy herds and flocks.
- Many livestock diseases can be transmitted to humans.
- Ambitious campaigns to eradicate ticks have largely given way to reducing tick numbers to tolerable levels.
- A few livestock diseases can be controlled through vaccinations.
- Most tick-borne diseases of livestock are contained by the use of organophosphate and pyrethroid dips.
- A tick-specific pesticide has yet to be found; all pesticides affect wildlife.
- Tick-borne diseases affect wildlife, occasionally leading to high mortality.

Lyme disease and other tick-borne diseases of humans are serious enough. But they are as nothing compared to the devastation by tick-borne disease of livestock. World-wide, the number and range of diseases carried by ticks exceeds those of all other invertebrates, bar none. Ticks ingest viruses, bacteria or minute worms while feeding on one host and subsequently transmit the microorganisms while preparing to feed on a second host. Once the microbe multiplies in the host's blood stream, other ticks feeding on the same animal will themselves become infected. Or again, in some cases the microbe may be passed from one generation of ticks to another through the tick's own ovaries, then to its fertilized eggs. From the tick's viewpoint, vertebrate land animals, mammals, birds and reptiles are little more than mobile canteens of highly nutritious blood. Optimum conditions to support a large population of well-fed ticks are achieved when compliant animals are herded together in large numbers. And few better conditions exist for ticks than in modern livestock farming.

The big killers

The big four tick-borne diseases of livestock, world-wide, are babesiosis, theileriosis, anaplasmosis, and cowdriosis. All affect a range of animals, domesticated and wild. A very brief account will put the severity of these diseases in perspective.

Babesiosis is a group of diseases often characterized by a reddish tinge to the urine of cattle (hence one of its names redwater fever) caused by the breakdown of red blood cells. Death follows from severe anaemia. One of these babesioses, Texas cattle fever, became part of the American cowboy folk lore in the late nineteenth century. There, enormous herds of docile cattle, mostly of European stock, were struck by ticks more used to struggling for a blood meal from migrating herds of bison. Within two weeks of being bitten the cattle became anaemic and listless with sunken eyes, twitching muscles and a characteristic gnashing of teeth. In susceptible herds where mortality exceeded 90%, the ranchers faced financial disaster. A century later, babesioses still stalk the plains. In recent years, over a million cattle in Australia and in Zimbabwe were lost before a related tick-borne babesia was brought under control.

Theileriosis is another protozoan disease of historic and disastrous proportions. In the 1890s in East Africa pioneering European settlers released their cattle onto grasslands alongside wild buffalo. The buffalo had long adapted to the local ticks but not so the cattle, mostly drawn from British breeds. The cattle quickly developed a tick-borne disease known as east coast fever. Within

78

five years it had spread southwards into the cattle herds of present-day Zimbabwe and by 1901 the disease had wiped out half of the livestock. Despite rigorous dipping programmes, an outbreak in 1989-1990 killed another 1.1 million cattle.

Anaplasmosis is a widespread disease of warm-temperate to sub-tropical regions resulting in severe anaemia and jaundice which, in acute cases, leads to death within 24 hours. If untreated, mortality can reach 50% or more. In 1986 up to 100,000 cattle in the USA were lost in one epidemic before the disease was brought under control.

Cowdriosis or heartwater is one of the most important livestock diseases in southern Africa. It has now spread to the Caribbean. It gets the name heartwater from the accumulation of fluids round the heart. Infected livestock, cattle, sheep and goats show characteristic twitching of muscles, loss of co-ordination and a high-stepping gait. Convulsion is followed by death. In acute cases the disease lasts for 6 to 7 days with 50 to 90% mortality.

While the headline figures of cattle mortality come from range farming countries, European farmers have to contend with related, though usually milder, diseases. Prevention is largely through pesticide dips or sprays. Treatment, where practical, is usually possible through antibiotics. However, to agriculture the cost of ticks is enormous. One estimate from the late 1980s put the world-wide cost of tick-borne diseases for cattle alone at today's equivalent of $10,000 million *annually*. The cost to wildlife is unknown.

Other tick-borne diseases—the exotic through to the disastrous

The big four diseases may dominate in the veterinary world but there are many, many more tick-borne diseases of livestock and wildlife which cause misery and death. As with Lyme disease, many names given to tick-borne diseases disguise their much wider distribution. African swine fever, first identified in Kenya in the 1920s, has now reached western Europe as far north as Belgium and is established in the European wild boar population. A similar disease of pigs has been recorded in the Caribbean and Brazil and there is considerable concern over its possible spread into the hog farms of the USA. Powassan, a small town in northern Ontario, gave its name to a human encephalitis—the disease has now been isolated from sick foxes, skunks and woodchucks as far south as Pennsylvania. In north-west Europe tick-borne fever is fairly common but mild in adult sheep. However, in certain countries such as Britain, it increases the susceptibility of lambs to other more serious diseases such as louping ill.

Today, louping ill is no longer thought of as a Scottish disease —the disease has been recognized from England, Wales and Ireland, with a similar disorder from coastal areas of Norway, Spain, Bulgaria and Turkey. Transmitted by the sheep tick, the virus infects sheep which, within three weeks, refuse to feed, develop muscular tremors and a leaping or louping gait. Mortality in flocks often exceeds 60% or more where the density of infected ticks is high. Those sheep which recover often show permanent neurological damage. In humans, the disease, usually seen as an encephalitis, has been reported from farmers, shepherds, vets and abattoir workers. It is, however, primarily a disease of sheep. Although sheep vaccines are available, veterinary treatment is not normally practised. Sick animals are usually isolated and destroyed.

Wild animals also suffer from the sheer misery of heavy infestations of ticks as well as tick-borne diseases. Seabirds seem particularly prone to heavy infestation. One colony of terns in Florida yielded 20,000 ticks *per square foot*! Not surprisingly desertion of cliff sites due to ticks occurs, resulting in the loss of thousands of eggs and fledglings. In woodland and moorland heavily infested with ticks, the young of many wild mammals, from mice to deer, may suffer severe loss of blood, a condition which can be fatal.

The solution

Fifty years ago the goal of livestock disease management was to eradicate ticks. Nothing less. Today, the approach to ticks is not eradication but to reduce their numbers to what are judged acceptable or tolerable levels. Quite apart from the cost, intensive control of ticks is increasingly being seen as undesirable because, once started, it can never be relaxed. When herds or flocks become free of ticks they lose immunity and this can expose livestock to catastrophic losses if ticks are re-introduced. The modern approach then is to be content with reducing tick numbers to tolerable levels.

Currently, there are two principal approaches or targets in the fight against ticks—each one with its drawbacks. The targets are the tick itself or the tick's food source, its host.

Targeting the tick

Pesticides

The history of pesticides has been the elusive search for a toxic compound which kills only its target species or, at the very least, breaks down to harmless substances after use. Sixty years ago, *the* anti-tick pesticide was arsenic. Unfortunately, it was lethal to livestock and to farmers as well as to ticks. Worse still it persisted in the soil and water courses indefinitely.

Shortly after World War II arsenic was widely replaced by DDT and other chlorinated hydrocarbon pesticides. These cheaply produced and widely available pesticides were liberally applied and, being relatively long-lived toxins, entered many food chains.

They became a disaster to wildlife and were banned in north America and western Europe from 1965.

The organophosphates became available during the 1960s and did not persist in the environment for as long as DDT. However, after a few years of use, as with arsenic and DDT, it also became apparent that insects and ticks were evolving resistance to organophosphates. In addition, in more recent years, there has been considerable concern over the safety of these pesticides to humans. By the 1970s, the pesticide industry began to offer pyrethrum for tick control—pyrethrum being a natural insecticide obtained from a relative of the chrysanthemums. Within ten years synthetic pyrethroids had been developed and products such as Permethrin, together with the organophosphates, are today the most widely used anti-tick pesticides. Resistance to pyrethroids, however, was recorded by the late 1980s and some five species of tick had developed resistance to organophosphates or organochlorides by 1995.

The latest generation of anti-tick pesticides, the avermectins, are based on a family of toxins found naturally in a soil bacterium. Products such as Ivermectin are hailed as 'the most effective parasiticides ever discovered'. Ivermectin is indeed lethal to ticks (and other invertebrates). At sub-lethal doses it inhibits tick mating, egg laying, even feeding. Unlike the earlier pesticides it is apparently harmless to vertebrates, though ecological and economic problems with Ivermectin, and its effect on non-target invertebrates, are now becoming apparent.

All of these organic pesticides, from DDT onwards, work by disrupting nerve function—just watch a pyrethroid-sprayed fly in spasm during its death throes. Modern pesticides do work well, however. Tick-borne babesiosis has been eradicated from nearly 30 million hectares of Argentina, partly through a 50-year programme based on compulsory pesticide cattle dipping.

Today, while dipping is still widely practised, pesticides are applied as sprays, pour-ons and spot-ons, through slow-release pesticide-impregnated collars and ear tags. Ivermectin is available in the form of implants, injections and in foodstuffs. The one area where anti-tick pesticides have not been widely successful is in aerial spraying. Unlike many pests of crops, ticks spend considerable periods, perhaps most of their lives, sheltering or resting at the base of vegetation where pesticide sprays do not penetrate.

Biological control
Here the aim is to employ a natural predator to control the target species. The household cat is perhaps one of the oldest biological controls exerted against mice. Though successfully used against certain insect pests, biological control of ticks has been limited. Perhaps the best example was the deliberate release of a chalcid wasp, *Hunterellus hookeri*, into eastern Massachusetts and western Montana in the 1920s, areas heavily infested with a particular disease-carrying tick. The intention was that the wasp would lay its eggs in the body of the adult tick and the emerging wasp larvae would then eat the tick from the inside out. The early results were encouraging but were eventually abandoned—despite repeated releases the wasp population did not survive.

The deliberate release of sterilized male or female ticks has also been tried in an attempt to break the reproductive cycle of the tick population. Again this approach has worked well with some insect pests; with ticks there has been mixed success. Sterilized males in one experiment lost their appetite for blood as well as sex and did not compete well with fully potent males. The release of sterilized females merely induced the potent males to try harder!

There has been interest in recent years in certain invertebrates which hunt out and eat ticks—such as fire ants and lycosoid spiders—and in plants which appear to be avoided by ticks. These interesting possibilities remain unexploited commercially.

Pheromones
Ticks regulate their urges to feed and reproduce through their

own chemical signals or pheromones. Many attempts have been made to exploit or disrupt tick behaviour through the application of natural and synthetic pheromones. Early attempts included attaching pheromone-baited beads to cattle—there the ticks were lured to the beads only to be killed by a contact pesticide. Impressive results have come from trials using pheromones targeted at the male ticks, drawing them away from females with a marked reduction in mating and egg production. Laboratory trials show up to 100% disruption of mating. This approach is encouraging where the male ticks attempt to mate on a large and compliant animal host. Unfortunately for Europeans, our sheep tick can and does mate off the host deep in vegetation. And something approaching 90% of female adult sheep ticks have successfully mated by the onset of winter each year.

Targeting the tick's food

Host eradication
The theory is that if the host is removed from an area then the cycle of tick development from larva to adult will be broken. One of the earliest documented attempts to eliminate the tick's food source—the host—started in Montana in 1911 in an attempt to control Rocky Mountain spotted fever. Ground squirrels, pine squirrels, chipmunks and other small animals—all hosts to one particular tick—were shot, trapped or poisoned on a wide scale and for several decades. The need to keep up the kill was because of the continued immigration of squirrels, chipmunks and so on, together with their ticks, from adjacent untreated areas. The practice was eventually scrapped as expensive and ineffective.

A less drastic approach than eradication has been to exclude the host, usually sheep or cattle, from tick-infested pasture for three months from mid-summer, preferably repeated for several years. Known as pasture rotation or spelling, it was widely practised in parts of Britain, at least in times of less-than-intensive animal husbandry. By removing the large animal host at the time of maximum numbers of maturing nymphs, the emerging adult ticks are deprived of their principal food source and fail to survive in large numbers. Exclusion of deer by fences is widespread in recreational areas of the eastern United States in attempts to reduce the incidence of Lyme disease.

One important message has emerged from host eradication campaigns—anti-tick programmes are unlikely to succeed if the targeted tick has an abundant wildlife host or hosts to feed on. In the case of the European sheep tick, its abundant wildlife hosts include field mice, bank voles, shrews, feral cats, grey squirrels and hedgehogs, pheasants, blackbirds and warblers. Tackling wildlife as a way of breaking the tick cycle is unlikely to gain public favour, short of a serious human health-threatening epidemic.

Improving host resistance

It has long been known that certain species or breeds of livestock show some degree of resistance to tick infestation. Zebu cattle (*Bos indicus*) are generally much less troubled by certain disease-carrying ticks than European breeds (*Bos taurus*) and cross-breeds with increased resistance have been introduced widely in the sub-tropics. The trouble is that this resistance appears to apply only to certain species of tick.

Another approach has been to vaccinate herds with extracts from ticks—inducing the livestock to produce their own anti-tick immune response in advance of a tick bite. When the cattle are subsequently bitten, the tick finds it difficult to draw blood and so dies. Field trials in Australia have shown an impressive reduction in tick infestation, although more recently there is evidence that some ticks are developing resistance even to these vaccines. Host resistance can also be achieved through the administration of drugs. Anti-parasite drugs such as oxytetracycline are used in cattle feeds and salt blocks in the USA but, inevitably, resistance to these drugs is developing.

Finally, ecologists have long recognized that ticks are important parasites in the well-being of wildlife. Indeed, much evidence has accumulated over many years showing that parasites such as ticks exert a considerable influence on the size of populations of many mammals and birds and on the behaviour of these species. Epidemics of tick-borne diseases among wild species have been recorded from time to time, most usually where there has been a high and very obvious mortality involving a collapse in the local population of, say, rabbits, hares, chipmunks or colonial nesting birds. There is evidence also that ticks may be important in controlling the movement and reproduction of a number of wild species in particular habitats; habitats which are heavily infested with ticks may be abandoned by the bird or mammal, with the loss of breeding grounds.

8
FUTURE PROSPECTS

> ### 🕷 Ticks—and how little we know
>
> - The relationship between ticks, as parasites, and their hosts, as a source of blood-meals, is an ancient one. No mammal or bird has evolved complete protection against ticks or tick-borne disease.
> - We are unable to predict, with reliability, the spread of tick-borne disease, particularly under changing climates.
> - We understand little of how ticks survive in the environment when not feeding. Could this be the key to controlling tick numbers?
> - We know little of how ticks interact with small wild mammals. Is this the key to tick success?
> - Tick control, in human health, will depend greatly on increasing public awareness of ticks and their diseases.

Most parasites and their hosts have a long and close relationship. They have evolved together. One of the theories underlying our understanding of evolution is that parasites and their hosts are locked into a perpetual arms race. For the host there is a never-ending search for new defences against parasites. Simultaneously, parasites continuously seek new ways to breach the host's ever-evolving resistance. At any one time some hosts will have genes which make them better able to resist parasites and they will breed to produce resistant offspring. Other individuals without this advantage will be more readily parasitized and will succumb. The theory runs to the core of biological evolution and holds that parasites, indeed, drive sexual reproduction (involving the acquisition of new genes for one's offspring) and in time, over many

87

generations, will result in the evolution of new species (an individual with enough new genes to differ significantly from its ancestors). Ticks fit the theories of evolution well.

Ticks have been actively challenging mammals and birds for many tens of millions of years. We can also say, with some confidence, that no mammal or bird has yet evolved which is wholly resistant to ticks or to tick-borne diseases. Seen against that background, we have to face up to the fact that our twentieth-century attempts to control ticks by pesticides, pheromones, manipulation of host or habitat are not likely seriously to disturb the age-old evolutionary relationship between ticks and their hosts. At very best we may succeed in tilting the tick-host relationship to favour the health of our livestock. We can provide answers to the ravages of tick-borne diseases in humans. But it is arrogance to think that we can make any lasting impact on the close relationship that has long existed between ticks, their hosts and tick-borne micro-organisms.

The way forward

Today we recognize that tick control through pesticide application, through host eradication campaigns or through methods of biological control have their limitations, Ivermectin included. Tick control using pheromones, while showing promise in small-scale, short-term experiments, has yet to be proven in wider trials.

Vaccination programmes have worked well to control many animal diseases but may be expensive and require repeated administration. However, advances in molecular biology make it likely that more effective and cheaper vaccines will be developed, at least against the most economically important diseases. Already molecular vaccines have been developed to control bovine and ovine tick-borne fevers in heartwater and redwater of cattle.

While we wait for new technological advances, an important development in the war against ticks in recent years has been what is called integrated pest control. This means tackling a population of ticks at several different levels. The control of Texas cattle fever in the USA and east coast fever in southern Africa, for example, is largely due to the combined effects of pesticides, the development of tick-resistant breeds of cattle and strict control over livestock movement. Integrated pest control is today well established in Lyme disease hot-spots in eastern USA. Reliance on one main method of control has proved, time after time, to be short-sighted and it is likely that integrated pest management will become the standard, particularly in large-scale farming.

The major contribution to tick control throughout the twentieth century, however, has come from a greater awareness of ticks among farmers and the public and our improved understanding of tick biology, ecology and disease transmission. This alone has done much to improve animal welfare. There are, however, many outstanding questions to be answered affecting not just the welfare of our livestock but also human health.

Paramount is our inability to predict, with any great accuracy, the spread of tick-borne disease and to forecast new epidemics. This is not just a problem of range or ranch farming in the tropics, it could become a significant problem in western Europe if recent patterns of climate change continue. Underlying our inability to predict changes in tick-borne disease and tick behaviour is our woefully sketchy idea of how ticks interact with wildlife. This is particularly true of the European sheep tick which relies on a variety of small wild mammals to sustain its early development and ultimately determines the size of the tick population. True integration of pest control methods may well depend on understanding how ticks have their being when not on the backs of sheep or cattle or the legs of walkers. In addition, despite a hundred years of experience with outbreaks of tick-borne diseases in places as dissimilar as Montana and Harare, Adelaide or Galloway, we still fail to predict epidemics. In part this is because we lack a full picture of the distribution of many tick-borne diseases, veterinary and medical. This information is, perhaps, the key to disease forecasting.

Although ticks, in terms of economics, are primarily a problem for livestock, it may be that the impetus—and the research money—for answering these outstanding questions will yet come through our concerns over ticks in relation to human health. Animal health is not generally an issue which concerns the public at large. But when there is a link between animal and human health, attitudes do change. And it may well be that recent concerns over Lyme disease, not itself a significant scourge of livestock, will do much to generate the search for new solutions to the problem of living with ticks.

Ultimately, however, as far as human health is concerned there can be no substitute for public health education—for the individual to be aware of the potential dangers of tick bites—and for the individual to balance worries over tick-borne disease with a common-sense approach to health during work and recreation in rural areas.

APPENDIX
Ticks of Mainland Britain and its Islands

Common name	Zoological name	Main UK habitat	Principal host	Diseases carried	Bites humans
Hard ticks					
Long-legged bat tick	Ixodes vespertilionis	Bat caves Wales & SW	Bats	TBE virus	-
Brown dog tick	Rhipicephalus sanguineus	Kennels S England	Dogs	Dog babesiosis & rickettsiosis	yes
Ornate cow tick	Dermacentor reticulatus	Pastures Wales & SW	Cattle, dog sheep, horse	Redwater fever, canine babesiosis	yes
Cormorant tick	Ixodes unicavatus	Rocky coastal nesting sites	Sea birds	Little known	-
Fox tick	Ixodes canisuga	Kennels, lairs UK-wide	Dogs, foxes badgers, cats	Badger babesiosis	-
Hedgehog tick	Ixodes hexagomus	Suburbs to forests	Dogs, small mammals	Lyme disease and others	yes
Marsh tick	Ixodes apronophorus	East Anglian marshes	Waterside mammals	Water vole tularemia	-
Northern bird tick	Ixodes caledonicus	Nests & roosts in north	Pigeons, seabirds	Little known	-

Passerine tick	*Ixodes frontalis*	Parks, gardens woods	Migrant and resident birds	Q-fever	-
Puffin tick	*Ixodes rothschildi*	Puffin burrows Wales & SW	Puffins, shearwaters	Several viruses	-
Rabbit tick	*Ixodes ventalloi*	Rabbit burrows SW England	Rabbits, cats lizards	Eyach virus	yes
Red sheep tick	*Haemaphysalis punctata*	Pastures Wales & SE	Sheep, cattle birds	Louping ill Lyme disease	yes
Rodent tick	*Ixodes acuminatus*	Burrows, nests SW England	Small rodents	Lyme disease	yes
Sand martin tick	*Ixodes lividus*	Sand martin burrows	Sand martins Great tits	RSSE virus	-
Seabird tick	*Ixodes uriae*	Coastal nesting sites	Cliff-nesting sea birds	Lyme disease & many viruses	yes and painful
Sheep tick	*Ixodes ricinus*	Moist grass & moorland	Many mammals birds, reptiles	Lyme disease Louping ill	yes
Two-host tick	*Hyalomma marginatum*	Migrant birds from the south	Birds	Haemorrhagic fevers	yes
Tree-hole tick	*Ixodes arboricola*	Nests, roosts S England	Hole-nesting birds	TBE virus	-
Vole tick	*Ixodes trianguliceps*	Forests, rodent nests	Small mammals	Louping ill Lyme disease	yes

Common name	Zoological name	Main UK habitat	Principal host	Diseases carried	Bites humans
Soft ticks					
Marine argasid	Ornithodoros maritimus	Coasts	Seabirds esp. gulls	Several viruses	yes
Pigeon tick	Argas reflexus	Pigeon roost SE England	Pigeons doves, hens	Fowl diseases Lyme disease	yes and painful
Short-legged bat tick	Argas vespertilionis	Caves, house & church roofs	Bats	Bat diseases rabies (?)	yes and painful

Note: The list of diseases carried by most ticks described here may understate the true picture, particularly the long list of diseases transmitted by the sheep tick. In addition several species of tick are known to carry diseases in continental Europe which have not yet been recorded in Britain. On human biting, the symbol – means that either biting of humans has not been recorded or is uncommon. Finally, there are two or three species which have not yet been recorded in Britain but are present in compatible habitats in France and Germany and which feed on livestock. These ticks could well enter the British list. The common names given here are those used by Hillyard (1996).

FURTHER READING

A great deal has been written about ticks particularly in the medical, veterinary and entomological literature. The following short selection covers a broad area of the literature and gives the opportunity to explore particular aspects more deeply.

Among the more accessible literature and written with the informed lay reader in mind:

Kantor F S (1994) Disarming Lyme disease. *Scientific American*, September, 34–38.
Schmidt K (1997) If you go down to the woods today. *New Scientist*, November 15th, 44–48.

And for rather more detailed or specialist information:

Axelford J S and Rees D H E (eds) (1993) *Lyme Borreliosis*, Nato Advanced Workshop, Series A Life Sciences, vol 260, Plenum Press, New York.
Benenson A S (1995) *Control of Communicable Diseases Manual*, American Public Health Association, Washington.
Gray J S (1991). The development and seasonal activity of the tick Ixodes ricinus: a vector of Lyme borreliosis. *Review of Medical and Veterinary Entomology* 79, 323–333.
Hillyard P D (1996) *Ticks of North-west Europe*, Field Studies Council, Shrewsbury.
Lane R S, Piesman J & Burgdorfer W (1991) Lyme borreliosis: relation of its causitive agent to its vector and hosts in North America and Europe. *Annual Reviews of Entomology*, 36, 587–609.
Lane R P & Crosskey R W (eds) (1993) *Medical Insects and Arachnids*, Chapman & Hall, London.

Kettle D S (1995) *Medical and Veterinary Entomology*, 2nd edn. CAB International, Wallingford.

Nutall P A *et al* (1994) Adaptations of arboviruses to ticks. *Journal of Medical Entomology*, **31**, 1-9.

Oliver J H (1989) Biology and systematics of ticks (Acari: Ixodida). *Annual Reviews of Ecology and Systematics*, **20**, 397-430.

Ostfeld R S (1997) Ecology of Lyme disease risk. *American Scientist*, **85**, 338-341.

Purnell R E (1980) Tick-borne diseases. *British Veterinary Journal* **137**, 221-240.

Sonenshine D E (1991) *Biology of Ticks*, Vol 1 & 2, Oxford University Press, Oxford.

Steere A C (1989) Lyme disease. *New England Journal of Medicine*, **321**, 586-596.

In addition occasional short Newsletters are published by the Institute of Virology and Environmental Microbiology, Oxford, under its Lyme Borreliosis Project.